My Family
Right or Wrong

MY FAMILY RIGHT OR WRONG

First British Edition published 1983 by
Bachman & Turner
53 High Street,
Maidstone, Kent, England

ISBN 0 85974 115 X

Translation by Miriam Arad

Typesetting by V & L Typesetting, Chatham.

Printed and bound in Great Britain by
Biddles Ltd., Guildford and King's Lynn.

My Family
Right or Wrong

by

EPHRAIM KISHON

Bachman & Turner

CONTENTS

A Father is Born

That morning at six the little woman sat up in bed, stared intently for a while at nothing in particular, then touched my shoulder.

"It's started," she said, "Call a taxi."

I rose unhurriedly, made the call and returned to dress, mumbling some words of encouragement at my wife, if only for form's sake. After all, we are both sane, intelligent people who know that childbirth is a simple biological process, nothing to make a fuss about.

"How about taking some magazines, dear," I suggested, "in case you have to wait . . ."

Everything went according to plan. The taxi arrived promptly, we made the hospital in good time, Information took the little woman's particulars and sent her off to have her baby. I was about to follow but Info stopped me.

"You stay outside," he told me, "You are no longer needed."

He was right, of course: at this late stage in the proceedings the male only gets in the way. My wife was of the same opinion:

"Just go home and do your work as usual," she said, "And then just go to the movies or something. Have fun."

We shook hands, I kissed her on the forehead and we said goodbye. You may perhaps think me cold and unfeeling, but I can't help it, that's the way I am: rational, sober, adult — a man!

The little woman had meanwhile vanished beyond some

door, and I began to take stock of my surroundings. Some dozen pale candidates for fatherhood sat chain-smoking on a bench opposite Info, as if their sitting there could make any difference. Every minute or so a fresh male would burst through the door and throw Info a single word: "Well?"

Whereupon Info would glance at the list on his desk, pick his teeth awhile, yawn at length, and finally announce: "A girl. Seven pounds two."

Following which the new father would jump into my lap and whisper raptly: "Seven-two! Seven-two!" The fool. What's it matter how much a baby weighs? Mine can weigh ten pounds for all I care.

I decided I'd go home and work as usual and stop wasting my time here. I'd run out of cigarettes too. Then it occurred to me that it might be bad manners to leave without saying hullo to the doctor. He might even need some advice or what. I went and found him and introduced myself, but the doctor seemed to be in a hurry.

"Call up some time after five," he said curtly, *"After*. Not *before."*

In that case there really was no point in staying, so I went home, sat down at my desk, and started to work as usual. Before long I realized that my brain wouldn't co-operate, which was odd, since as a rule it's a very obedient animal, my brain is. What on earth could be the reason? Hadn't I slept well, perhaps? Some atmospheric disturbance? Or could it be the fact that my wife was having a baby? I didn't quite rule out this last possibility because well, I mean, there's no point in being *too* complacent. This is an event, after all, a great event in which I am personally involved. Of course I'm sure the child will be normal and healthy, nice, but nothing special, a child like all others. A child. Going normally to college and then on to a diplomatic career. What'll I call him? Boaz? Elipheleth? No, better give him a name foreigners can spell, like Raphael, say, so that when he becomes Foreign Minister they'll be able to pronounce his name at the U.N. I won't let him marry young. And he'll have to know plenty of languages

6

and a bit of nuclear physics and such. Though of course I won't force him to do anything he doesn't want to, like if he'd rather study aerodynamics it's okay with me.

And what if it's a girl?

Really, it's time I asked. I pick up the receiver casually.

"Nothing yet," says Info, "Who's calling?"

There was a sort of muffled hoarseness in his voice, as if he were trying to hide something from me. I started leafing through the newspapers to calm my nerves. "Two-Headed Goat Born in Peru", splashed over three columns. Journalists! Hanging's too good for them! I jump into my car and drive straight to the hospital to talk to the doctor about goats.

"What now?" said the doctor crossly, "What are you doing here?"

"I just happened to be in the neighbourhood."

"I told you not to call before five! Know what? Don't call us, we'll call you!"

"Thanks, doctor, that's just what I came to ask: who calls whom?"

The doctor was right. I ought to go home. Very sensible man, this doctor. Silly to hang around here like all these guys on the bench. I sat down beside them for a moment just to see what it felt like. Someone was telling the others how this would be his third, he already had a boy and a girl (6.9 and 7.2 respectively). Superior ass. Others were passing snapshots around. I felt a bit out of it, but on a sudden inspiration pulled out my wife's X-rays taken in her ninth month.

"Cute," somebody remarked, "Looks like a strapping fellow."

I bought a new pack of cigarettes, but still had this nagging sense I was forgetting something important. I asked Info how about it but he only clicked his tongue, "tsk", so I upped and went to the movies.

A subtle drama about a boy who hates his father. Hollywood! Never mind, it's going to be a girl anyway. I can feel it in my bones. A girl. Ruth. Or Golda. Though she can be an archaeologist if she likes, just so long as she doesn't

7

marry a pilot. Pilots are out. Good Lord, before I know it I'll be a grandfather. Time flies. Why's it so dark in here, though? Where am I? Oh, at the movies. Some rubbishy film. Let's get out of here. What now? Look in at the hospital?

I went and bought a huge bunch of daisies, because a florist's delivery boy can always get into a hospital. "Room 24", I flung at Info and got past, hallelujah.

The doctor wasn't too happy to see me.

"What the hell do you think you're doing with those flowers?" he thundered, "There's nothing yet, so get out of here and stay out!"

I tried to explain that the flowers were just a trick, that I *knew* there was nothing yet, only I'd thought that maybe there *was* already. The doctor swore in Russian and left me. Out in the street I suddenly remembered what it was I had forgotten: I hadn't eaten all day. I went home quickly to get some food, but it turned out I wasn't hungry, so I only drank four glasses of water and went to sleep. Sleep! Ha! Why won't it come, that baby? Why won't it come already! I *know!* It's *twins!* That's it! Good! Two for the price of one. Their names? Let's see, what would be a good name for twins? Marks and Spencer? Oopsie and Daisy? They'll have a practical education. They'll be textile merchants and never know want. If only that queer buzzing in my ears would stop. And those spots swimming before my eyes. I ring Info. Nothing. Drop dead, you scoundrel! Just wait till my daughter is born and I'll show you!

Damn, now I've run out of cigarettes again. Where can I get a new pack at this time of night? Somewhere near the hospital maybe? I rush out but a neighbour hurries after me to say I've forgotten to put on my pants.

I burst out laughing, and am unable to stop till I get near the hospital, where I suddenly remember God. I don't pray very often, but this time I can't resist it.

"Please, Lord," I pray, "Let her be a normal boy with only one head, please. I'm not asking for myself, Lord, but for the country which needs healthy boys. Girls. Twins . . ."

At the hospital Info tsk's at me before I've even asked. Bang! I smash the door with one blow of my fist and burst through. Info shouts after me to stop but there's no stopping him, I mean me.

"Doctor!" I shriek, running through the white corridors, "Doctor!!"

"What's happened?" he says. "Oh, it's you. Listen, do I have to call the police to keep you out? What are you — a hysterical girl?"

Me? A girl? Me? What's the matter with the man? Doctors! I sit down on the bench and swear I won't budge till they hand that baby to me. Anyone here can spare me a cigarette? Info seems to get a fit from just looking at me. To hell with him! What if I'm a little excited and ask a little question now and then? This is my son's birthday, isn't it?

Eleven-thirty p.m. and still nothing. Lucky woman, the wife, to be spared this torment. O God, maybe they've found she isn't pregnant at all, she's just eaten too much popcorn or something. The cheats! No, I won't let the boy be a diplomat. Let her go to a kibbutz. I'd go myself if only I had a cigarette. My kingdom for a smoke. A horse. A goat. Hush-a-bye baby, diddle-o-din, your daddy is ripe for the loony-bin.

With great difficulty I open my eyes and drag myself to Info's desk. I can't even speak any longer, I just blink.

"Yes," he says, "A boy."

"What?" I say, "Where?"

"A boy," says Info, "Eight pounds."

"Why? How?"

"Listen, are you Mr. Kishon or aren't you?"

"Dunno . . . perhaps . . . Wait!"

I pull out my identity card. He's right! I'm Mr. Kishon. Kishon, that's me.

"Yes," I say, "So?"

"You have a boy!" Info shouts, "A boy! Eight pounds! A boy! Get it?"

I throw my arms about his neck and want to kiss him but he won't let me. Then I rush out into the dark night. The street is empty. *Now* it's empty! Streets! Who'd believe I could still turn cartwheels! At last a policeman comes and calls me to order. I kiss him.

"Eight pounds!" I shout at him, *"Eight pounds!"*

"Congratulations!" says the cop and produces a snapshot of his daughter.

A Chip of the Old Block

Every premiere is an exciting event, but what's a mere play to the greatest show on earth: the first appearance of a new baby before his loving relatives?

The little woman had presented Rafi to the nation in the middle of the night, and they told me I'd have to wait till morning to see him. The doctor had said I'd better come alone the first time, so I didn't take anyone along except my mother, because she's my mother, and my parents-in-law because they, too, had suddenly become grandparents. Also Aunt Ilka and Uncle Jake, because they'd never have forgiven me if I'd left them out, and the Zieglers who'd brought such a darling little romping suit, consisting of white booties, a bonnet, and the cutest blue panties you ever saw.

By a curious coincidence, we received exactly the same present from my mother, as well as from Aunt Ilka and Uncle Jake, not to mention scores of friends and acquaintances. And the milkman. In a way we felt it was a pity the child would grow up, as otherwise he'd be equipped with warm clothing for life. One thing is certain, though: any baby born within the circle of my friends in the near future will receive a darling little romping suit from me.

Naturally I didn't come to my wife empty-handed. At one moment during those difficult hours on the bench I'd promised myself I'd buy her a mink-coat if she brought it off, but this was the morning after, and I remembered soberly that summer was just round the corner, and she'd look pretty silly wearing

11

furs in a heatwave. Instead, I went to the fanciest jeweller's in town and chose a smashing diamond necklace, which seemed just the thing till I saw the price-tag. Really, who does the woman think I am? Rockefeller? Just because she's given birth to a baby? She's not the first woman who has, and they don't all get diamonds for it, do they?

In the end I bought her some smashing carnations tied with a fancy ribbon, and a banana for Rafi. I also put on a dark suit to show my appreciation for her efforts. I felt so full of goodwill towards her that I even decided not to tell her what I'd gone through last night.

On the way to hospital my mother urged us to keep a distance of no less than two yards between us and the baby, because she was sure we were all crawling with microbes. Stung to the quick — crawling? *crawling?* — Aunt Ilka said she only hoped my mother wasn't like some grandparents she knew, and wouldn't start going pootshiemootshie over Rafi, which would be a sure way of spoiling him from birth. What with one thing and another, our tempers were rather strained by the time we arrived at the hospital.

Information had had a hard night and was dozing, so we slipped by *en masse,* and a nurse showed us to the little woman's room. We knocked reverently on the door, but she wasn't in. Uncle Jake, who has two terms of pharmacology to his credit, said she'd probably been taken off for a post-natal check.

At that moment Aunt Ilka, who'd stayed a little behind still nursing her grudge, gave a great triumphant shout:

"Here! He's here!"

We rushed over and there . . . on an outsize tea-trolley . . . swaddled in white from top to toe like a cocoon . . .

"My God" — my little wife's mother whispered — "The child! Isn't he sweet! Isn't he grandma's own pootshie-mootshie!"

"Little heart of mine" — my mother breathed — "Little heart of mine . . ."

"Can't see a thing," said I, whereupon Aunt Ilka snorted

that of course I couldn't, nobody could, the way they'd bundled him up, and gingerly pulled down the blanket and fainted with bliss.

There was Rafi.

Rafi himself.

Like a little angel.

With a halo round his head.

My mother-in-law broke into sobs.

"Ach," she sobbed, "He's the image of poor Uncle Paul . . . Look at that nose! . . . And the mouth! . . ."

"And the ears!" her husband muttered, "Just like his grandma's."

"Rubbish," Jake protested, "The chin is pure Victor. That's just how he used to stick out his chin when he got a bad hand at poker."

"And I say," thus Mrs. Ziegler, "that he's the spitting image of his mother. Those eyes! Just look how he opens and shuts them . . . Exactly like she does. Opens them . . . shuts them . . ."

I myself kept quiet because frankly, I felt a bit confused. When I'd first set eyes on Rafi just now, I'd heard a big bell tolling in my head, saying bing-bong, this is no joke, this is your son, old man, and I'd lost my heart to Rafi then and there. On the other hand, he — well, how shall I put it — with those great bags under his eyes, and his red, bald, toothless and crumpled appearance altogether, he actually looked like nothing so much as a wizened stockbroker. I hasten to add that of course he was a cute little miniature broker, very cherubic and all, but I was a bit disappointed in him all the same. Deep in my heart I'd hoped that as soon as he saw me he'd cry "Daddy, daddy!" Then the child opened its mouth and broke into loud wails.

"You see his palate?" Aunt Ilka cooed, "Just like poor Andy's."

Why deny it: we were all profoundly moved. After all, it is surely marvellous that all the physical and spiritual traits of his ancestors should be incorporated in one such tiny tot. It's a miracle, really, the way Nature . . .

"Excuse me," a nurse interrupted my reflections at this point, and started walking away with the tea-trolley.

"Please," I asked, "Where is Mrs. Kishon?"

"Mrs. Kishon?"

"Yes, Isn't this Mrs. Kishon's son?"

"This? No. This one belongs to Fortuna Mizrahi. And anyhow, it's a girl."

And with that she took the little monster off.

Something ought to be done about the anarchy in our hospitals.

Dress Rehearsal

"Ephraim," the little woman called out from the bedroom, "I'm nearly ready."

The time was 9.30 p.m., Wednesday, December 31. The wife had been standing in front of the wardrobe since dusk, getting ready for a New Year's party at Tibi's. I reminded her that we'd promised Tibi to be there at ten, but the little one said it was all right to come fifteen minutes late, everyone did, parties were always dull at first anyhow, they took time to warm up.

"All I have is old rags," the little one concluded sadly, "I've got nothing to wear."

She says this every time we go out, never mind that her wardrobe is bursting with clothes. The idea behind the nothing-to-wear remark is to make me doubt my adequacy as a provider, and to undermine my self-confidence in general. Personally I don't know one dress from another, I think they're all terrible, and yet I'm always called upon to help her choose which one to wear.

"It's either the plain black," the little one muses aloud, "or the blue with the slit."

"That's it," I say, "with the slit."

"It's too dressy, though. How about the chemise?"

"Yes," I say, "that sounds fine."

"Not too sophisticated?"

"Sophisticated?" I demand, "Not at all!"

What the hell *is* a chemise anyway. I zip her up and go to the bathroom to shave, while she looks for another pair of

15

nylons to go with the chemise thing. In the end she finds one that's the right colour, but it has no mate. It's an axiom: the best stockings are always single. It follows that she can't wear the chemise but must look for another rag to go with the pearls she received for her birthday from her husband's wife.

"It's ten," I warn her, "We'll be late!"

"Stop fussing," thus she, "So you'll miss two dirty jokes, so what?"

I have already put on my good pants, but the wife is still debating the question: pearls or silver brooch? The pearls are nicer, but the brooch is more intriguing. It'll be a miracle if we make it by eleven. I start reading the dailies. The wife is looking for a belt to go with the brooch, but gives up in despair because she has no handbag to go with her new chamois. I start writing some letters, a short story, a sketch . . .

"I'll be ready in a jiffy," the wife calls from the bedroom, "Come and do up my zipper."

What do all those divorcees do whose husbands have escaped in good time? Who zips them up? They probably don't go to New Year parties. Neither will we. The woman ties a little plastic cape round her neck and starts on her make-up. That's to say — not the make-up proper yet, only the foundation-laying. Meanwhile her eyes search for shoes to go with the bag. The beige are at the cobbler's, the black with the high heels are divine but you can't move a step in them, the low heels you *can* move in but they're low . . .

"Eleven o'clock!" I announce, "I'm giving you five minutes. If you're not ready by then I'll go alone!"

"I'll be ready," she calls from the bedroom, "And you can't do the twist anyway."

She removes the little plastic cape because she's decided to go in the plain black after all. But where are the nylons to go with it? Where are her dark nylons? Eleven thirty. I resolve on a trick: I get up, walk with heavy tread to the door, shout a furious goodbye, slam the door on the inside — and stand still in the passage holding my breath . . . I suppose she's cracking, the little one is. Good. Treat 'em rough, I say. Like Nietzsche

16

with his whip.

Five minutes pass in absolute silence. It'll be awkward if I have to spend the rest of my life in a dark passage. Maybe something has happened to her . . .

"Ephraim," the wife calls, "Come and do up my zipper!" She is back in the chemise. (The plain black has bust a seam.) She's changed nylons as well, and is in a quandary about the pearls.

"Make yourself useful, can't you," she says. "Help me. What do you suggest?"

I suggest we go to bed and have a good night's sleep. I, for one, am changing into my pyjamas.

"Don't be silly," the little one says crossly, "I'll be ready in ten minutes."

Twelve o'clock. Church bells are ringing in the new year. Goodnight. I turn over and go to sleep. The last thing I see is my wife in the plastic cape, doing her eyebrows. I loathe that plastic cape the way no plastic cape was ever loathed before. I sleep, and dream I'm Charles Laughton chopping off the heads of all my six wives. I mean his, Henry the Eighth's wives. All six of them keep changing their nylons on the way to the scaffold. One of them is doing her nails . . .

I sleep on soundly for an hour and a bit, and wake up next year. The wife is in front of the mirror in the blue with the slit, painting her eyebrows with a burnt match. She's mad. I've married a madwoman.

I glance at my watch: one fifteen. A horrible thought flashes through my mind: I'm in hell! I'm in a hell like in Sartre's "No Exit", where the sinner's worst punishment is to be shut up in a room with a woman who keeps dressing-dressing-dressing — *for ever!*

I'm beginning to feel a bit scared of her. Just now she's transferring the entire contents of her big black handbag to her small black handbag. She's almost dressed already — wait! — except for her hairdo. The great question is: swept down over her forehead or up and back? Down or up? Wee Willie Winkie runs through the town/Shall it be up, or shall it

17

be down?

"I'll be ready in a jiffy," she tells me, "Get up!"

"Think there's any point going still?"

"What do you mean point going? Then what am I hurrying for? Don't worry, they'll have left you some of those sickening cocktail sausages!"

She's a bit annoyed with me, I know, because why am I so impatient. The little plastic cape is on the floor by the bed. Quietly I stick out a foot, fish it up with my toes, and sneak off to the kitchen, where I burn the horror with my own hands. I put it in the sink and set a match to it and watch it burn like Nero saw Rome burn. It leaves a bad smell in the kitchen but I don't care — this is one thing I've always wanted to do. I return to the bedroom and find the little one before the mirror in a near-finished state. I zip up the back of the plain black and start dressing myself, barely able to keep my eyes open, when — oops!

A ladder!

I can just see it from behind. She has — a ladder — in her left nylon. Omegod! Because as the proverb says: Plus ça change le nylons, she'll plus change her whole outfit again. Please God, let her not discover the ladder. Let her discover it only at the party. It's not such a terrible ladder, Lord, it's only in the back. Make a miracle, Lord . . . I tiptoe away to the study and sit down at my desk.

"Don't waste time now," the wife calls out from the bedroom, "What are you doing there?"

"I'm writing a movie script."

"But I'm nearly ready!"

"Yeah . . ."

I'm getting into my stride. There's this great artist — painter, musician, humorist, whatever — a man of vast promise who gets bogged down somehow and fails to make it. And why? Because of a woman, ladies and gentlemen, a woman. A burden. A cross. I write effortlessly, ideas just flow from my pen. The artist realizes his plight and resolves to cut himself loose from the woman, the burden, the cross. One sleepless

18

night he says to himself, "Boy," he says to himself, "It's now or never, so grab your pants and get the hell out of here!"

Holy Smoke!

The wife is in the bathroom *washing her face*. Two. It's two o'clock. She feels that the colour of her eyelashes is a shade vulgar and wants to put on new make-up. For that a person must wash his face and start from scratch — foundation, powder, the lot. Despair grips me. I go to the wardrobe, pick a strong necktie and fasten it to the curtainrod. Enough . . .

The wife hears me climbing on a chair.

"Stop it," she says, "and come do my zipper. So what are you whining for now?"

What am I whining for? Hell, do I know what I'm whining for at 2.30 in the morning, got up in a clean white shirt, a dark jacket and striped pyjama pants, while my wife sprays her hair with one hand and fumbles in a drawer for gloves with the other? Gloves. Did I say gloves? It's hard to believe, but it really looks as if we'd come to the end of the road. A flicker of hope lights up my darkness. So my suffering hasn't been in vain after all. *She is actually ready.* In a moment we shall go out and have fun. Bursting with energy, the little one transfers the contents of her small black handbag to her big black handbag and takes off the pearls. Everything is becoming a bit hazy. The dawn is breaking, the church bells ring one-two-three. Happy New Year. The little one says cheer up, and why haven't I shaved?

"I have," I whisper, "Once upon a time when you started dressing — I shaved." I go to the bathroom and shave again, I have aged this night. The face of a haggard old man is looking out at me from the mirror — the face of a man who has known torture — the face of a husband.

"Why do I always have to wait for you?" the wife demands from the bedroom. While waiting, she looks for a hat because her hair hasn't come out right. Now. A last glance in the mirror, a last dab at her cheeks, a light brush of powder . . . Right . . . Who knows, maybe there's still some brandy left at Tibi's . . . Are we going? . . . Yes, let's go . . .

The door opens. Impossible! We're off! We're off to the party!

"Wait!" The wife stops, thunderstruck. "I've got a ladder in my left nylon!"

Here, at this point, right on my own doorstep, the Great Zipper finally caught up with me. The rest is silence.

Miching Mallecho

Rafi himself turned out to be a handsome baby, extremely bright and active, and an expert maid-remover. No sooner would a prospective char cross our doorstep than Rafi, prompted by a mysterious instinct, would launch into his famous nonstop solo, whereupon the candidate would blink and say:

"You do live a bit far out of town, don't you . . ." and dissolve into her elements.

Still, somebody up there loved us after all, because one day Latifa showed up and announced that her sister Ethroga had sent her. Ethroga was a young lady who had done for us some three years ago, much as she hated our brooms. Now she had apparently decided to let her sister loose on us by way of revenge. The sister, Latifa, was a big woman with a cunning smile. Her Hebrew was rather poor, and she had a tendency to lapse into colloquial Arabic midway through a sentence, which made her all the more useful in our mixed Israeli-Hungarian household. For once Rafi was caught napping: we talked with Latifa for half an hour and he didn't let out a peep, with the result that Latifa stayed. She wasn't exactly God's gift to womankind, as it turned out, but could mop a floor or get through a pile of laundry with reasonable efficiency, though the expression on her face made it clear she could think of better ways to spend her life than up to her elbows in a tubful of nappies.

Trouble first cropped up when we decided to move the furniture around. The reason was that our livingroom had become a garage for prams, our bedroom was flowing with milk bottles and talcum, the playpen was in the kitchen and the kitchen in the bathroom. We were all busily pushing things about when the little woman asked Latifa would she put up the mirror in that corner there.

"What?" demanded Latifa, "Hang a *mirror* in a *corner?* You looking for trouble, madam?"

She went on to describe in vivid detail how a neighbour of hers, a Mrs. Mazal, had actually gone and hung a mirror in a corner though she, Latifa, had warned her repeatedly against it, and how less than a week later Mazal's husband had won ten thousand pounds in the lottery, and how the shock of it had done for his heart and he had died like a dog, poor man. That shook us rather. We decided not to tempt the devil, and just to play it safe we sold the mirror to the rag-and-bones man for a song.

The next crisis came only three days later, when we asked Latifa to dust the ceiling. This time she almost got angry.

"Madam," thus Latifa, "Me I don't get up on no ladders in a house what's got a baby in it! All I need is he'll crawl under it and remain a midget for life like in the circus."

"Now, now," we said, "Now, now."

"Now-now nothing! Listen, the tailor what lives near the market — he's got a boy 15 years old and three foots tall. Three foots! And why? On account of he kept running under ladders. So. You want to make a midget of the little pootshie — Latifa can't stop you, but Latifa sure ain't cleaning no ceilings in this house!"

The same fate befell our window panes. Latifa declared that only a raving lunatic would clean windows on a Friday, when it was common knowledge that it made terrible fires break out in a house. As well burn down the whole place ourselves! We were getting a bit tired of Latifa and her doomsday warnings, and tried to persuade her to defy the evil spirits just for once, whereupon Latifa told us that if we could show her a single char who'd do windows on a Friday, *she* would pay *us* on the first of the month instead of us her.

22

We glanced out and what did we see? At the druggist's across the street the maid was cleaning windows.

"Yah!" Latifa declared in disgust, "They make fire insurance on Thursday, they clean windows on Friday, them crooks!"

We paid *her,* and our windows remained dirty too, so in order to let in some light we asked Latifa a few days later to take down the curtains. Latifa was thunderstruck.

"God-o-God!" she breathed, "Take down the curtains in January? You crazy or something, madam? You want the poor mite to get some awful sickness? You want to God forbid lose your Rafi?"

This time, however, we stood our ground. We told Latifa in plain words that we didn't believe in any of that evil-eye rubbish, and anyway the doctor lived practically next door. Latifa said she was sorry, but she couldn't take such a crime upon her conscience. We assured her that we would take full responsibility for the consequences.

"All right," said Latifa, "You give it to me in writing."

I sat down at my desk and wrote out a formal statement to the effect that Mrs. Latifa Kurdani had warned us of the danger to our child's health if we took down the curtains, but we had forced her to carry out this operation against her will. We both affixed our signatures to this document, whereupon Latifa morosely took down the curtains.

Towards evening Rafi grew restless, and at night he ran a fever. Next morning the thermometer read 104 degrees. Latifa took the news calmly, but gave us a look that made us squirm.

The little woman fetched the doctor, who diagnosed flu. "But how could he have caught it?" the wife said anxiously, "We are so careful with him!"

"How?" Latifa piped up, "I'll tell you, Mister Doctor! They made me take down the curtains, that's how!"

"What's that?" the doctor asked, "Curtains?"

"Yes, Mister Doctor," thus Latifa, "Taking down curtains in January they was, with a little baby right here in the house!"

We made signs for her to cut it out and go back to the

kitchen, please.

"She's right, you know," the doctor said, "Taking down curtains in this weather and no doubt letting in a draught . . . No wonder the child caught a cold. Very unwise, I must say."

Words fail to describe the look on Latifa's face as she produced her document and showed the doctor our signatures.

Since then we no longer argue with Latifa. We accept the fact that doing the washing on Sunday brings floods, and take it for gospel that polishing doorhandles in winter is as good as inviting snakes into the house. Last week she announced that if we wanted the child to get well we shouldn't sweep the floor for twenty-eight days.

And that's where matters stand. Latifa comes in every morning, drops into an armchair and watches TV. The place is getting filthier by the day, but Rafi's cough is definitely improving, knock on wood.

The Writing Through the Wall

We generally get on very well with our neighbours, especially with those next door, the Seligs, whom we can't stand. They're all right, I mean, but they have this radio, and he, Felix Selig, comes home every day at 6 p.m., walks straight over to it and turns it on. Full blast. He doesn't care *what* it is — music, and-here's-the-headlines, Landmarks in Literature — so long as he gets it loud and clear.

And that's how we get it too.

The little woman, who is on sugar-borrowing terms with Erna Selig and hence in and out of their flat, claims the whole thing is based on an acoustic riddle. It's a fact, she says, that the noise is much louder in our place than in theirs. Be that as it may, the wall between the two flats is so thin that we put out the light when we undress for fear the Seligs should see our silhouettes on the bedroom wall. It needs no saying that the least whisper is audible on the other side, let alone a radio turned on full blast at 6 p.m. We felt that only a miracle could save us.

* * *

And the miracle happened.

I had bought two tickets for the theatre, and on the appointed evening the woman told me to look at myself, to just look at myself, Ephraim, so I went to shave. I plug in my electric razor, and what do you know — the Seligs' radio sets up a terrific racket. I pull the plug out — the racket stops. I start again — *it* starts again. Next Felix Selig's voice comes through the wall: "You hear that racket, Erna? It'll drive me

25

nuts!"

Exciting vistas opened.

Next day at 6 p.m. I was stripped for action, razor in hand, loaded and cocked. Felix came home and turned on the radio full blast. I counted ten and plugged in the razor — and in our neighbours' flat a quartet in C-minor turned into a rat-tat-tat major. Felix waited awhile, deluding himself that the noise would go away. Like fun it would! In the end he broke down and yelled at the radio: "Stop, dammit!"

His voice was so compelling that I instinctively pulled out the plug. Felix switched the radio off, and I glued my ear to the wall: this was the critical moment. He called his wife and told her in a hoarse voice:

"Listen, Erna, the queerest thing. I yelled at the radio to stop — and it stopped!"

"I bet," said Erna. "You are working too hard, Felix, and you don't sleep nearly enough. Tonight . . ."

"Don't baby me!" Felix said irritably, "I swear it happened. Here, listen."

And he switched on the monster again. I could almost see them sitting there, waiting for the rat-tat-tat. This time I counted twenty, to heighten the suspense.

"Na," said Erna, "Nothing."

"*Now* there isn't, when I want to show you!" poor Felix said bitterly, and turned to the radio: "When I *want* you to do it you don't, ha?"

I plugged in. Rat-tat-tat.

"Good gracious!" said Erna softly, "It's eerie . . . Now tell it to stop . . ."

"Stop!" Felix told the radio in a shaky whisper, "Stop . . . please . . ."

I pulled out the plug.

* * *

Next day I met Felix on the stairs. He was looking definitely out of sorts and had dark rings under his eyes. We mentioned the weather and had just started on the Middle East when Felix asked did I believe in the supernatural.

26

"Hell, no," I said, "Why do you ask?"

"I just sort of wondered."

"My grandpa, though," I went on, "He did."

"Did what? Believe in spirits and all?"

"Well, no . . . No, he had this fancy that inanimate objects — things like, you know, tables, typewriters, gramophones — had souls of their own. Crazy, isn't it? What's the matter, Mr. Selig?"

"N . . . n . . . nothing . . ."

"Gramps used to swear that his gramophone hated him. Ever heard such rubbish?"

"*Hated* him?"

"Mind you," I added, "He *did* die in rather peculiar circumstances. He was found dead on the floor one night, with his hands like trying to reach that gramophone. The turn-table was still spinning."

"Please," said Felix, "I don't feel well."

I had to help him up the stairs, he was trembling so. At home I made a dash for the drawer, grabbed my little electric Hitchcock, and took up position by the wall, the eager little woman beside me. Felix switched on the radio. "You hate me!" my wretched neighbour cried, "I'm sure you hate me, right?"

Rat-tat-tat. I let the message sink in, then removed the plug.

"But why? What have we done to you?" Erna Selig pleaded, "Aren't you happy with us?"

Rat-tat-tat. The Seligs were cracking up, searching feverishly for all sorts of sins they might have committed to deserve this. When Erna started on about that time they hadn't eaten *kosher* on *Shabbes,* I decided the time was ripe. The little woman went out for a little neighbourly call on the Seligs, and I could clearly hear them telling her how something had taken over their radio, and had she ever heard of inanimate objects having souls?

My wife, the little minx, heard them out, then suggested *talking* to the radio. It might listen to reason.

"*You* talk to it," they said, "Please. We're too scared of him."

The little woman switched him on. This was It.

"Great Spirit of the Radio," my wife said, "Can you hear me? Give me a sign!"

Plug in. Rat-tat-tat.

"Thank you."

Plug out.

"Great Spirit!" my wife called, "Give me a sign: do you want these people to play your radio more? (No sign.) Do you want them to play it louder? (No sign.) Then perhaps you don't want them to play it all – ever again? . . ."

Plug in.

Plug in!

PLUG IN!

Silence. No rat-tat-tat. Nothing!

The razor wasn't working. It wasn't working! It had broken down! For six years it had worked perfectly, and now . . . *now* . . . kaput!

"Can't you hear me, Spirit?" my wife called, "I asked: Do you want the Seligs to stop using their radio. Answer me! . . . Nu?"

I plugged in, out, in. I shook the stupid thing, knocked it, beat it. Nothing. I broke out in a cold sweat. Did they *have* a soul, then? . . .

"Rat-tat-tat!" the wife shouted at the top of her voice, "Give me a sign, you fool! They should shut up their radio for good! Ephra-im!"

She was overdoing it, rather. The Seligs turned off their mystery radio and looked at my wife askance.

I had the razor repaired overnight, and blow the costs.

"The condenser was burnt out," my technician explained next day, "I replaced it, and I'm sure it'll put an end to that rat-tat-tat noise you had on the radio too."

Selig is back full blast, and as for inanimate things: maybe they have a soul – a sense of humour they haven't.

Regina

Now that we had a baby, we needed a baby-sitter, and as we always bought the best for our Rafi we naturally took Regina Fleischhacker. Regina is a pro. She's loyal, she's punctual, she can change a nappy with a flick of the wrist, and she hates TV. Rafi has never said a word against her yet.

Still, nobody is perfect, and the trouble in Regina's case is that she lives way out in the wilderness of Suburbia, at a place called Holon. The only way she can get to us is by cab, but sometimes she can't find one and has to squeeze into a crowded, smelly bus, and on those occasions she arrives at our place in a state of shock, her eyes filled with mute reproach:

"Couldn't get a cab again."

That always makes us feel terribly guilty, so round about eight p.m. we start praying there should be a cab, and sometimes it helps and there is. It follows that we worry a lot about the Regina-problem, because she has no peer. She has no telephone either. And she lives way out in Holon.

So?

So we decide to go to the movies, say, and we invite Regina for 8.30. So after supper I sit down to write a couple of very urgent letters, say, but it's uphill work and I can't get them right. Regina nevertheless arrives on the dot of 8.30, and one look at her face tells us it's been a No-Cab Day again.

"I ran," she pants, "I ran like crazy to get here on time." Obviously the proper thing to do now is to up and storm out of the house, in order to justify her having run like crazy. The thing is that I'm still sweating over these urgent letters, and

29

they've absolutely got to be finished tonight. They're urgent, right? The little woman is standing over me with a whip: "Come on," she says, "Hurry up, hurry up, she'll be wild!" And sure enough, Regina appears in the doorway:

"You still here?"

"We're almost . . ."

"No, no, take your time. I only wonder why, if you're in no hurry, I must run over here like crazy . . ."

"We're just about . . ."

"I mean, why call me at all if you're staying home anyhow?"

"We'll pay you, though . . . even if . . ."

"Don't pay me, madam!" says Regina Fleischhacker grandly, "I am not in the habit of taking money for not working! Next time kindly think twice before you ask me to come!"

I can sense Holon and its dearth of taxicabs coming next, so I snatch up the typewriter and we beat it out of the house, and I finish my letters at the pastry shop across the street.

By then it's too late for the movie too, and the little woman suggests we kill three hours — which is your professional baby-sitter's minimum — taking a nice little walk through the streets of Tel Aviv. It's a lovely place, is Tel Aviv. Especially along the seashore, the northern suburbs, the south, the east, and the centre. We return at midnight like two weary bats and pay Regina her full 55.75 pounds.

"When will you be needing me again?" Regina enquires. The little woman waits for me to decide. Why do *I* always have to decide everything? And if I make a mistake it's fatal, because Regina has no phone: you fix a date with her — it's final.

"Day after tomorrow?" she offers helpfully, "At eight?"

"I suppose so," I mumble, "We'll go to the movies . . ."

* * *

God moves in mysterious ways, and no kidding.

On the day after tomorrow at seven I started aching all over. I felt positively ill, and I think I even ran a temperature. My loving wife stood by my bed full of concern:

"You'll have to get up," she said anxiously, "She'll be

30

here any minute . . ."

"But I'm ill!"

"I can't help that. Pull yourself together or something. I don't know *what* she'll say if she finds she's come all the way from Holon for nothing again."

"I feel dizzy."

"So do I. Take an aspirin. Get up, *get up* . . ."

Regina arrived at eight like a Swiss watch, ticking loudly: "Good evening. Couldn't find a . . ."

I dressed in alarm. If she *had* found a cab we might have considered trying something — begging, bargaining, dunno — but now, what with the buses so crowded and all, it was out of the question. We left post-haste. Outside I leaned against a wall, too weak to stand. I felt really rotten, caught the flu or what. Well, what now? Not to the movies anyhow, I felt bad enough as it was.

"Right," said the woman, "Then how about a little walk?"

"The only walking I'll do is up to bed."

So we got into our car and I lay down on the back seat. I'm fairly tall and our car is a mini. "O Lord," I pleaded, "Why do I have to double up in this car when Thou knowest I have the flu?" The Lord didn't answer, and after a round 75 minutes I'd had it.

"Woman," I groaned, "I'm going in."

"Already?" the little one demanded from the driver's seat, "We've only been away an hour and a half. Do you expect her to come all the way from Holon for that?"

"I don't expect anything," I whispered, "But I'm damned if I'll die for Fleischhacker. I'm still young. I've still got a lot of living to do. I'm going in, woman."

"No, please, just another 20 minutes."

"I can't."

"Know what?" the little one said, catching up with me on our doorstep, "Let's try and slip in behind her back . . . We can sit quietly in the bedroom and wait . . ."

Hm, no bad idea. We opened the door gingerly and tiptoed in. The light in my study was on, so we knew where the enemy was. We moved with the utmost caution, taking advantage of every irregularity in the terrain like in the best war flicks, but a few steps off target disaster struck. Why do they always put this aspidistra bang in the middle of the passage?

"Who's that?" Regina screamed, *"Who is that?"*

We turned on the light.

"It's only us," the wife called out quickly, "Ephraim forgot to take the present."

What present? The woman threw me a shut-up sort of look, went to the bookshelf, and after a moment's hesitation pulled out "The History of the English Theatre, 1616–1962". Then we said sorry, and left with the book. Out on the landing I felt my knees buckle, and the first red dots polkaed before my eyes. One of my wisdom teeth began to hurt too. I collapsed on a stair and I think I started to cry. I had a fever and all.

"It was the only thing to do," the woman said apologetically, and passed a cool hand over my hot forehead, "Buck up, only an hour and a bit to go."

"If I survive," I swore, "We'll move to Holon — right across the street from Regina Fleischhacker!"

Our neighbour Felix Selig came down the stairs.

"What's the matter? Lost your keys?"

"No," we said, "It's all right."

What fools we are: we should have asked him for political asylum! "Mind if we stay at your place for an hour?" we should have said, "We'll sit quietly in the kitchen and never disturb you." Oh well, it's the staircase for us. We talked of Regina. She's a real personality. A lady. Only why can't we persuade her to take money even if we do stay at home? Why do we always have to get out the moment she appears? Why can she never find a cab? Why are these stairs so deadly cold? Them is tough questions, them is.

Ten minutes later (two hours and a quarter in all) I got up and said I was ready for another try. Now I already knew where the aspidistra was . . .

This time it worked.

Our rich experience in do-it-yourself breaking and entering stood us in good stead. The door closed behind us with the faintest of clicks, we crawled past the study unnoticed, made the bedroom as planned, stretched out on our beds and waited for the three hours to be up. The little woman stared at her watch counting minutes, while I leafed through "The History of the English Theatre, 1616–1962" by moonlight . . .

At this point there is a certain gap in my memory.

"Ephraim!" I suddenly heard my wife's excited whisper, "It's five thirty!"

I blinked at the blaze of sunlight coming in through the windows and stretched myself. I hadn't had such a good night's sleep in ages. Our strategic position, on the other hand, didn't bear thinking on. How the hell do we get home now? Can't cross the passage to the front door in broad daylight without Regina catching us, but we obviously can't stay holed up here till darkness either.

"We'll have to get Regina out of there somehow," the little one mused, "Wait . . ."

And with that she stole out and slipped into Rafi's room. Two tense seconds later our baby broke out into piercing shrieks. The little woman popped back into our room.

"Pinched him?"

"What else?"

Regina jumped up and swept into the nursery. We used the momentary confusion to scramble for the front door, go out and come back again calling out a cheerful "Good morning!"

"Is this a time to come home?" a bleary-eyed Regina asked, confronting us with an indignant Rafi in her arms (thank God he can't talk yet), "Where have you been?"

"At an orgy."

"The youth of today!" Regina clicked her tongue and presented the bill. Then she stepped out into the morning to look for a cab to Holon, and I daresay she didn't find one.

Just a Little Spring Cleaning

Sunday. — This morning the little woman said: "Passover or not, I don't intend to turn the whole house upside down this year. It's a sad flat that's done only once a year, spring-cleaning is all very well but it's expensive, and I know it upsets you, dear. So I'll just give the place a good sweeping out and that's all. You don't have to do anything except please fix the broom because it sort of wobbles, okay?"

"Okay," I said, and went right off to buy her two long-haired, artistic-looking brooms to show her how much I appreciated her housewifely restraint. When I came back I found a small brook meandering in front of the house. It turned out my wife had thought she might as well give the floors a good wash before sweeping them, and had taken on a couple of women — one to wash and one to fetch water — but the water-fetcher worked faster — hence the brook.

"We'll be through in a day," thus the little one, "No big to-do or anything."

I was glad of that because we only had fried eggs for dinner and that's not enough for a grown man like me. Somebody'd also taken down the shutters because they creaked. The locksmith said we wanted new hinge-pins, the old ones were rusted, I'd have to go get them at Fuhrman's in Jaffa, he had no time to run around looking for no blooming hinge-pins. Okay.

Monday. — Returned from Fuhrman's with the hinge-pins at noon. The brook had swollen to a river. I couldn't get in by the front door because the passage was blocked by our armchairs on account of the upholsterer. I jumped in through the bathroom window and fell into the quicklime, which the painter was stirring in the tub.

"I thought," said my wife, "that as long as we were cleaning the place we'd better give the walls a new coat too, but that'll be all." She asked me to go talk to the painter about his fee because that was a man's job. We settled for 5,000 Israeli pounds, doors and all.

The locksmith glanced at the hinge-pins and said they were two-inch while he needed three-inch ones, and sent me back to Fuhrman's. The little woman took Rafi from his temporary bed on the bookshelf and camped down with him in the playpen. I spent the night on my desk between the stove and the best tea-service. Slept badly. Fried eggs for dinner again.

Tuesday. – Fuhrman said those first hinge-pins had been three-inch after all and sent me back. On the way home I stepped into the tar puddle in our garden and had one hell of a time cleaning it off in the living-room where the bathroom now was because in the bathroom they were changing the tiles (IL. 3,540). Get it all over at once, said the wife. The electrician we'd called for a short circuit told us we'd better change all these old Hillary casings we had in our walls, they were none too safe, and in that case he'd recommend matching them with Hilloa switches and Hillbilly tubes – IL. 1,800 in all. The locksmith said the hinge-pins were three inches all right, but British inches, while he'd meant German inches. Back to Fuhrman's.

The painter was halfway through the kitchen ceiling when he raised his fees.

"I always raise them a couple of weeks before Passover," he explained, "on account of how everybody figures they better not wait till Passover, 'cause then there's always a big rush on house-painters and they raise their fees, so everybody wants me a couple of weeks before Passover and so that's when I raise them . . ."

He also asked would I get him a tin of Polychrome from this shop on Herzl as he couldn't waste his time, and also some turpentine please, a new brush and two packs of Camels. The brook ladies had meanwhile grown from a duo to a quartet and had burst into song.

I solved the sleep problem too. I simply emptied the contents of the wardrobe into the fridge, put the wardrobe face up on the balcony, and promptly fell into a deep mothball-drugged sleep. I dreamt I'd died and was being carried to the grave by a solemn procession of craftsmen and hillbillies.

Soft eggs for dinner.

Wednesday. – Fuhrman informed me that as far as hinge-pins are concerned there's no difference between British and German inches and sent me from here to eternity. When I told the locksmith what Fuhrman had said he looked puzzled and asked what the hinge-pins were for. I explained about the shutters, but he couldn't get in to fix them because someone had taken up the floor tiles. My wife had always wanted a blue-and-beige floor (IL. 6,200) instead of our dull old grey, and it was now or never. "Just this," she said, "and that's it." Okay. Not counting myself, there were 16 people working in the flat now, though we couldn't do much talking on account of the men tearing down the walls. .

"I talked to a contractor who's almost like an architect," thus the little one, "and he advised pulling down the wall between Rafi's room and your study to make one big living room, so then we wouldn't need what's the living room now because we don't want *two* big rooms, so we can divide that up by a wall – and then Rafi'd have a room and you'd have a study!"

I took a ladder and a pair of scissors and cut down all the lampshades in the house. Let's leave nothing undone, say I. The almost-architect (1190) said (950) why not (712) move the kitchen to the attic and the attic to the john. I said: Dunno, better talk to my wife because she doesn't want to make a big to-do of it this year. Raw eggs.

Thursday. – Didn't get home from Fuhrman's today. Slept on a bench in the park, ate grass, drank water from the sprinkler like the birds. Delicious. Felt reborn.

Friday. – Surprise, surprise! When I came home there was nothing left of it except a hole in the ground. My wife was in the garden with Rafi.

"I thought: we're doing the house anyway," she said, "so let's knock it all down and start from scratch . . ."

I said okay, but let's wait till after Passover on account of the lower fees, and she said certainly, dear, and put Rafi down under a tree and started dusting the leaves.

A Little Adultery Goes a Long Way

This year we decided to spend our holiday in a nice family *pension*. We picked a solid, sober little place in Lower Galilee, far from the madding crowd, the wagging tongues, the lot. I rang up in good time and booked us a double room.

"Very well, sir," said the Desk, "A double room. Will you be arriving together, please?"

I said naturally, what else?

So we arrive at the little place, report to the Desk, sign the ledger, and the Desk hands us *two* keys and says: "I've given you No. 17, sir. The lady is in 203."

"What the hell," I say, "I asked you for a double room, didn't I, not two singles!"

"You mean you want to be together in one room?"

"Of course we do! We're married. This is my wife."

The Desk slips out from behind the desk to glance at the tags on our luggage. Good Lord! I suddenly remember the little one has borrowed a suitcase from her mother, and the tag reads "Erna Spitz". The Desk straightens up and sends us a scathing look.

"Very well," he says, "A double room. Here's your key, *Mrs.* Kishon!"

"Listen," I say uneasily, "Would you like to see our identity cards?"

"No," says the Desk with a world-weary sigh, "Go ahead, I'm not the morals squad . . ."

Nor, it turns out, are the guests in the lobby. All eyes follow us as we walk across, mouths twist in ironic yet approving grins. Only then do I notice that the little one has come in that flaming red dress of hers, and that her heels are far too high. Damn! That big bald party over there — some filthy rich exporter, I'd say — cocks an eyebrow at us and whispers something to the smashing blonde at his side. Ugh! A sweet young thing like that going for a dirty old lecher like him when the country is full of nice young men like me. Fie on it!

"Ephraim!"

I turn round. It's Buckteeth Jr. Sits there winking at me and making signs of "Wow! Some dish!" The idiot. I mean, my wife is all right and all that, but a dish? Idiot. What's the matter with everybody?

Things get even worse during dinner. As we walk demurely to our table, we catch scraps of conversation that make our ears tingle: "Left his wife at home with the baby, and toddles off with" . . . "A bit plump, isn't she, but I hear he likes them that way" . . . "Taking a double room, bold as brass" . . . "Some nerve" . . . "I know his wife. A great woman — and he comes here with this tootsie. Ah, men, men" . . .

Buckteeth Jr., it now appears, isn't alone either. He's got some painted doll in tow who's wearing a rather too ostentatious wedding ring on her finger. He introduces her to us as his sister. Sister my foot! I introduce the wife. Buckteeth bends gallantly over her hand and gives her a seductive smile. After dinner he draws me aside. "Everything all right at home?" he asks in a man-to-man whisper, "How's the wife?"

"You should know. You've just kissed her hand, for Pete's sake!"

"Ho ho," says Buckteeth and stands me a vodka at the bar. He tells me I don't have to put on an act with him, he wasn't born yesterday, ho ho, and anyhow, he doesn't think I'm really being unfaithful to my wife, not really. He's sure this is just a little side-step, very healthy for the good old marriage, actually, everybody does it, ho ho, nothing to it. He, Buckteeth, is ready to bet my wife would forgive me if she ever found out.

"But she *is* my wife, you fool!"

"Come off it!"

And he gives me up in disgust. I return to my wife and he to his "sister". The swarm of males who've meanwhile been paying court to my little one drift away reluctantly, leaving her radiant. She tells me that one of them — rather handsome, you know, in a Robert Redford sort of way — has been urging her to "drop that silly-looking character you are with" and move in with him.

"I said no, of course," she giggles, "I mean, he's nice, but he lisps."

"And is that your only reason? Me being your husband doesn't count?"

"Oh, yes," she remembers, "So you are. It's all so confusing . . ."

The bald party sidles up to us and introduces his blonde bombshell.

"Permit me," he says, "My daughter."

The old phony. "My daughter!" She doesn't even look like him. She's got hair, to start with.

"My girl," I introduce the little one in turn, "Miss Erna Spitz."

It didn't take my wife long to adapt herself to her new status as my mistress. Whenever I tried to embrace her in public she'd pull away, telling me to consider her reputation. Once after supper I pinched her cheek and she slapped my hand and got quite angry:

"Don't flaunt it!" she hissed, "There's gossip enough about us as it is!"

She had a point there. Rumour had it, for instance, that we'd gone swimming one night without a stitch on. I also heard it said I was trying to get her on pot. Buckteeth Jr.'s "sister" asked was it true the little one's husband had smelled a rat, had pursued us to Tiberias, and we'd escaped by the skin of our teeth and come here?

"Well," I said "Not exactly. It's true her husband went to Tiberias, but with their *maid*. So then what happened was

— the maid's boyfriend went after them and took her back, so then hubby decided to take his revenge on *us*, and it's been a merry chase ever since . . ."

The "sister" swore she wouldn't give us away and went off hugging her news. Fifteen minutes later the Desk called us and asked nervously whether it wouldn't be a good idea for us to after all move into separate rooms now, "just for appearances' sake".

"No," I said, "We'll face it together!"

The little one, meanwhile, was getting to be quite a handful. She started ordering the most expensive dishes and would drink nothing but "bubbly", as she called it. Next she wanted some "trinkets", and just a "teeny-weeny little minkie".

"Just look," she pouted, "Look what Baldie gives *his* 'daughter'!"

Then the bottom dropped out of our little love-nest.

One day our company was joined by a reporter for one of the tabloids who knows everybody, but everybody, in this country.

"What a dump," he complained after he'd done a quick recce of the place, "It's too bloody boring for words. Buckteeth is here with his sister, you're with your wife, and that bald judge over there has his daughter in tow. You're a regular bunch of saints here. I'm surprised you stood it so long, old boy."

"Ha ha," we said, "Ho ho."

Before long everybody's spirits began to droop. The women all turned into ordinary housewives, the men into husbands. Soon afterwards we left for home. And now to top it all my wife keeps saying I've been unfaithful to her with *her!*

Man and Supermarket

Israelis are great bargain-hunters, like who isn't. It follows that when the first supermarket opened in Tel Aviv with a lot of hoopla, a sweeping urge gripped the nation to go there and buy, buy, buy. We, the little woman and I, held out for three days, but then our resistance broke down. Just to be on the safe side, though, we left our wallets at home and took Rafi with us instead.

Frankly speaking we *were* rather dazzled by the place. It was a lot bigger than our corner grocery, and quite a bit cleaner too. And all those bright colours! And those loaded shelves! The only trouble was — it was terribly crowded in there and we soon felt like ... like ...

"Sardines!" cried the little woman and pounced on a shelf overflowing with grab-happy housewives and an international sardine-show. There were tins and tins of them: Spanish sardines, Portuguese sardines, Yugoslav, Albanian, Cypriot, Israeli sardines. They were swimming, variously, in oil, brine, ketchup, and "natural juices", presumably sea water. My wife picked one Yugoslav and two Swedes. And one more. And another.

"We were about to run out of sardines anyway," she explained, "and they're so much cheaper here ..."

"But we didn't take any money!"

She lowered her eyes:

"I've just found some loose change in my pocket ..."

Trust a woman! Ha!

She had meanwhile gone and found an empty cart as well

42

and dropped the dozen tins of sardines into it, along with one Golden Syrup and a bottle of shampoo. Then she looked up and her eyes widened:

"Good gracious!" she whispered, "Where's Rafi?"

Our little darling was gone! How too awful! I could just picture him — a mere scrap of a child toddling among all those people at knee-height and biting their legs. Awful! "Rafi!" we called desperately, "Ra-fi!"

"Toys to your left," an experienced salesgirl informed us. All at once we heard a thundering crash, and sighed with relief. We knew what had happened: Rafi had discovered the Great Tin Mountain — an ingeniously constructed pyramid of 5,000 food-cans reaching to the ceiling. He, Rafi, had cleverly yanked out the bottom ones, and the rest had come tumbling after. We quickly bought him some candy to comfort him. Also honey, Swiss chocolate, Dutch cocoa, Indian tea and coffee to dry his tears. Then, as we were piling the loot on our trolley, my fingers suddenly touched a bottle of perfume, a pocket-thriller, and 20 lbs. of beetroot.

"Woman," I said, "This isn't our cart!"

"Suppose it isn't," thus she, "So what?"

We'd made quite a good swop, actually. Our new cart held some lovely cheese, sliced peaches, a plastic dog-leash, and a pail.

"Goodie!" my wife said happily, "Only how'll we pay for all this?"

"Um," I said, "I do have a few loose pounds on me somewhere . . ."

We moved on, but were soon halted again by a traffic snarl, brought on by two loaded carts slamming into each other head-on. We drew nearer because we love a good fight, but . . .

"Rafi!" cried the little woman, "Rafi!"

This time we turned him up in the erstwhile egg department.

"Whose child is this?" the scrambled egg salesman demanded furiously.

"Dadadadada," said Rafi, pointing a sticky finger at himself.

We dragged him away, along with some washing powder guaranteed-to-remove-all-stains, and returned cartwards. Someone had meanwhile added a few bottles of brandy, a mop, and table salt to it. We put our little egghead on top, and to boost his morale bought him a rocking-horse and a pair of slippers for me.

"More!" the little woman grunted and pushed two virgin carts towards the meat counter. I felt sort of pleasantly intoxicated myself. We bought us a chicken, lamb, liver, tongue, goose breast, and goose legs, wings, head and shoulders, a turkey, ducks and drakes, and also some fish, a salmon, a trout, hogfish, dogfish, goatfish, perch, tuna, and whale. And a little caviar. And mussels. And crab. Then we bought some eggplant, paprika, onions, capers, wool, cinnamon, vanillin, vaseline, beans, peas, figs, lemons, a canary, records, op, pop, barley-corn, spinach, buttons, string, rope, jam, treacle, soap, soup, nuts, strawberries, ice-cream, laurel, hardy, cucumbers, curtains, a sword, a pipe, mushrooms, a piper, olives, cherries, pears, pomegranates, handgrenades, bulbs, cotton, an aquarium, chopsticks, fiddlesticks, tyres, wires, starch, carbon dioxide, and bread.

"It's worth every penny of it," the woman would point out from time to time, "Things are so much cheaper here . . ." I dragged our six-cart caravan along panting, and struggling with the calf that we'd tied on at the end because we also like schnitzel. On the way to the checking-out counter we topped our cargo with a few rubber-stockings and some floor wax. I also saw the cutest light switch ever and tried to get it off the wall but they'd screwed it on tight. A pity. I asked a salesclerk to help me but he said, "Sorry. Can't move out from behind this counter. Sold my pants."

While the girl added up our bill on one of those nice jumping paper snakes the little woman stocked up on microscopes and chips. I added a Geiger counter for good measure.

I was afraid all these trifles would add up to quite a sum, but in the end it only came to 40,000 pounds and a bit. We were just admiring the speed with which the salesgirls were packing the stuff in those tall brown paper bags when we missed Rafi again.

"Anyone seen a little boy around here?" we asked the girls.

"Wait," said one of them, "Is he blond?"

"Yes. And he bites."

"That's him then," said the girl and opened one of the paper bags. Inside sat Rafi, calmly eating toothpaste.

"Sorry," said the girl, "Didn't realize you'd brought him with you."

They promptly paid back the money they'd charged for Rafi (72.30 pounds), and we left. Two lorries were waiting outside to drive us home with the goods. Tomorrow we're starting a grocery.

Eyewash

"Ephraim," the little woman asked, "Do you think I'm pretty?"

"Yes," I said, "Why?"

It turns out she's been brooding over this delicate question since April last. She knows, according to her, that she is nothing special, but still, she has *got* something. Or would have, she dare say, if it weren't for those spectacles . . .

"Men seldom make passes," she tells me, "at girls who wear glasses."

She's quoting, of course. She's quoting all the time, especially newspaper ads extolling the greatest invention since the wheel: *contact lenses.* They are just the right thing for People Who Care: two tiny bits of glass instead of those big clumsy spectacles You've Always Hated. You simply put them right on your eyeballs and nobody sees a thing, whereas you see everything. It's terrific, it's a real must, particularly for myopic actresses, beauty queens and spinsters. "This mannequin," the little one's girlfriends tell her, "Started on them only four months back and already she's divorced a South American millionaire . . ." Everybody recommends the Miracle Lens. Don't hide Those Lovely Eyes behind a pair of specs. Try it. Buy it.

"I've heard of this optician," says the wife, "You coming too?"

"Me?"

"Whom do you think I want to look pretty for?"

Me. We found some three dozen clients in the op's waiting

46

room, nearly all of them old hands. Some had got so used to their contact lenses they didn't even know whether they were in or out. That was presumably what they'd come to the optician to find out, because, I mean, what else could have brought them here? One elderly lensbearer was showing us all how easy it was: He put the little disc on his fingertip, see? and then – now watch! – he moved it right into his open eye and – oops! – where is it? It's dropped to the floor! Nobody move! *Nobody move!*

We seized our chance and moved in to the contact man. He seemed a nice cheerful young fellow, bursting with faith in the future of the lens. "It's very simple, really," he explained, "One's eye gets used gradually to the presence of a foreign body in it, and soon it all becomes the most natural thing in the world . . ."

"Wait a minute," I said *"How soon?"*

"Well . . . that depends . . ."

He then carried out a few opti-tests on the woman's eyes and declared them eminently lens-receptive. Next he showed us how to place the disc on the tip of one's finger, and how to remove it again six hours later by pulling the eyelid to one side. My wife was breathing hard, but there was nothing she wouldn't do for the cause, and a week later, to be sure, she went back and received her very own contact lenses in a sweet little plastic case, against the round sum of 4,500 pounds. That same evening she started the gradual breaking-in process: on the first day – 15 minutes, on the second – 20, on the third . . .

The third? Forget it.

In other words, it's all a question of staying-power. The wife rinsed her lenses as instructed, placed one of them on the tip of her finger, then pointed it at her right eyeball in a dramatic *J'accuse!* Then what happens? The nearer the finger comes the larger it gets – larger and larger, like in the movies, till in the end it's so huge it's ghastly. "Ephraim," the wife whispered, "I'm scared of my own finger . . ."

I said never mind, for 4,500 pounds I'd stick it.

The little one pulled herself together, looked her finger straight in the eye, and — oops! — just as the finger arrived her glance sheered off and the lens plopped onto the no-man's-land white of her eye. She never was much of a marksman, my wife. It took the best part of an hour for the lenses to settle into place, but then — oh glory! No spectacles, but a pair of shining eyes looking at the world in expectant delight.

Naturally there was still some teething-trouble, such as the fact that the woman kept her face turned rigidly skywards like a sunflower, which is a very pretty flower, I don't say it isn't, and also that she couldn't move her eyeballs but kept staring fixedly at a single spot in space. Also that she couldn't blink? Blink? *Any* movement *whatever,* even rubbing her toes, brought on the most excruciating pain in her eyes. The little one therefore sat on a chair like a frozen fish, a prayer in her streaming eyes: "Pass, fifteen minutes, pass!" And then they were mercifully past and she quickly removed the lenses . . .

That's to say, she wanted to remove them, but the ornery little things were quite happy where they were. The poor woman pulled her eyelids one way, as the young conman had shown her, she pulled them the other way — the lenses only laughed and stayed put.

"Don't just stand there," she cried in a panic, "Do something! *Do something!*"

I was getting quite flustered myself. She was going through hell for *me,* after all. I looked frantically for some useful instrument but only found a pair of pliers with one pli missing, and her all the time weeping and weeping.

"Ouch!" she cries, "Ouch!"

I rang up the hospital.

"Help!" I shouted into the phone, "A pair of contact lenses have dropped into my wife's eyes. Come quick!"

"Shucks," thus the hospital, "Go to your optician, mister."

I carried the wife over my shoulder to the car and raced to the op. He whipped out the little beasts in a second flat and told us we hadn't done badly for a first time, and to carry on, undaunted. He even presented us with a minuscule rubber pump, something like the gadget you use for unclogging the kitchen sink, only smaller. You plant this little pumpkin on the lens, you get suction, and the rest is child's play. Good.

We went home, and the poor thing spent the rest of the day bathing her eyes. During the next few days I learnt what a lot of punishment the human eye can take. Every morning my little one would overcome her fear of the dragon finger and bravely insert the beasts. Then she'd very carefully get up from before the mirror and stagger to my room with her face turned stiffly at the ceiling, glassy eyes brimming over, stand before me, poor fish, and demand girlishly: "Now guess: are they in or aren't they? . . ."

That's because she had read in the advertisements how it's impossible to spot the presence of contact lenses with the naked eye. That's what makes them so popular, see? I'm sure that people who visited us at that stormy time will never forget the sight of the weeping woman drifting through the house like Niobe, all tears, and muttering: "I can't . . . I can't . . ."

She grew uglier by the day too. Her eyes were baggy and swollen, her nose purple with weeping, her shoulders bowed. Really, what that woman went through — the third degree is nothing to it! And the exercises kept getting longer every day. And afterwards always having to rush to the op yet to remove the lenses again. Because the pumpkin was a flop. The one and only time she tried it, she planted it on the lens, got suction and — shloop! — nearly sucked out the whole eye. Then there was that dark morning when the little one appeared in my study pale as a ghost and whispered:

"The left lens has got in behind my eye . . . It's in my head now . . ."

Hop to the op, who said no, a thing like that couldn't happen, the human eye was sealed hermetically in back, she'd probably just lost her lens like they all did.

The little one insisted, though.

"I've searched the whole house," she said, "I *know* it's in my head!"

She could even hear it rattling inside. Personally I didn't believe her, but was rather inclined to accept the op's explanation, the more as I'd spotted the lost lens with my own eyes on our bathroom floor and had crushed it carefully underfoot. I therefore took my wife's tormented face between my loving hands and said:

"It's the finger of God. Return to your spectacles, child . . ."

And that was the end of the gradual exercises. Fifteen minutes on the first day, twenty minutes on the second, specs in a fortnight. Still, we didn't break all contact with the lenses. Why waste all that effort? So from time to time we show up at parties without any spectacles at all, and announce proudly that we're wearing our lenses now. The effect is tremendous — always provided we don't stumble over the furniture. People say isn't it wonderful, these lenses are quite invisible, and right away ask us for the address of our op. The wife herself is completely cured and as pretty as ever. I believe she's even grown a bit.

Dip-Happy

The weatherman had applied lots of atmospheric pressure that year and given us a rainy winter, which was all very well for the crops but hell for our bathroom boiler, because it smoked when the wind blew. The little woman complained that it looked like nothing on earth, ugh, it was all black, and it used to be such a nice silver colour, remember? I therefore decided I'd surprise her and paint it over nicely for Passover.

I resolved, what's more, to do the painting myself, because a professional will demand 250 quid for a little job like that without turning a hair. I therefore went and bought an enormous can of Aluminium Silver Paint, guaranteed fireproof, shockproof and all, as well as a sleek and thirsty-looking brush.

Next morning when the wife had gone to work to earn her taxes, I opened the can, stirred well, dipped the brush in the shiny liquid and began to paint the boiler. The effect was splendid: a smooth even surface entirely eclipsing the sooty mess underneath. I don't want to take all the credit for myself — anyone of average intelligence, an I.Q. of 140, say, could have done it. You simply couldn't go wrong with this aluminium stuff, it as good as painted itself. Try it: you'll never want to touch anything else, including paint. I'd got so much satisfaction from my work that I just couldn't sit around and "wait till the first coat dries properly", like those finicky fusspots said on the label, but went right back and applied a second coat to my boiler, and then a third for good measure. Then I noticed that the bathroom taps looked rather shabby too, so I restored them to their former glory with a few strokes of the brush. Then I sat back and reasoned as follows:

My hands are dirty anyway, and the can is already open too. Why not look around the house and see if there's anything else that needs touching up, as long as I'm about it?

I therefore rose and started moving briskly through the place, silvering over two worn door-knobs, the kitchen tap, and three aluminium saucepans (they looked like new after treatment), then the cactus pot in the window along with the cactus spines, and a few knick-knacks here and there like a shoehorn, an ashtray, two stools and the kitchen table.

At this point I really wanted to stop, because I felt I was becoming addicted to the stuff, but then my glance fell on my old motorbike and the temptation proved too much. I wheeled it up to the porch and slapped silver paint all over its body and over the chain too, though this last, come to think of it, showed I was already well on the way to the loony-bin. It was too late to go on the wagon now, however, because the bike had dripped paint onto the porch-tiles, and the only thing to do was to go over the floor as well. In a fit of inspiration, I decided to skip every other tile, to obtain a charming chessboard.

After the chess I told myself sternly: "Enough!" but on my way to the bathroom to give the boiler a final once-over, it occurred to me there was no point painting only two of our door-knobs, and consequently did a couple of pictureframes too, and touched up our print of the Mona Lisa by dressing her in silver lamé, which went much better with the smile than her own rags.

While doing the radio I suddenly noticed that my shoes had sprouted silver freckles, so I painted them over for camouflage. They looked really handsome like that, and I won't be surprised if the idea catches on. ("Smart men wear aluminium-silver shoes!") After adding a touch of glamour to the Encyclopaedia Britannica, I decided to lay off, only just then my eye caught the lampshade, so I fetched the ladder. (Funny, you'd have sworn this ladder was made of silver, and yet it was made of wood.) I got up on it to paint the lampshade, and the light bulb (?), but as I stood there some paint spilled on our Persian rug. I'm sure you'll all be happy to know that Persian rugs absorb silver paint wonderfully well, though I don't know if that's due to the quality of the paint or of the rug.

At this stage in the boiler-painting I grew lavish and started squandering silver right and left with inflationary abandon. I did the wardrobe (it's been fireproof-shockproof ever since), then opened the wardrobe and spruced up all my wife's handbags and a few of my ties, and finally changed one fur coat from plain fox to silver fox. Next I rushed out into the garden and painted the fence, the tree-trunks, the tree-leaves, and the carnations. Just as I was putting a second coat on the shutters, the mailman came and I sprinkled some silver on his temples to make him look more distinguished, but the fool didn't get the point and fled screaming.

Round about noon it hit me that the walls were terribly out of keeping with the rest of the place now, and just as I started to put that right the door opened and my wife came in.

"I'm sorry," she said, "I thought this was my flat, sir."

She was about to turn away but I stopped her and explained that this was me, her husband, and it was a surprise for Passover. She was surprised all right, and wanted to pack at once and move to a hotel pending the divorce, but she couldn't on account of the paint not having dried on the suitcases yet. She then burst into tears and I sat down beside her and gently, tactfully, painted her fingernails silver.

Bottled Up

We all have our little weaknesses. Some people drink, some gamble, some chase skirts, some pants. My wife is fond of kittens. Not the pampered kind that wants to be stroked all day and goes "prrr" like an electric razor in love. No, she goes in for week-old strays mewing pitiably on streetcorners. When the little woman catches sight of a poor little waif like that, her heart melts, tears shine in her eyes like diamonds, she takes the orphan home and cares for it with endless devotion till it grows up to be an eight-day-old cat, that's to say next morning, when she gets bored with it and tells her husband:

"Why do I always have to do everything myself?"

That's the way it happened with Pussy.

This particular bit of fluff got itself picked up one morning on the corner of Herzl and Bialik. Black and very thin it was, and playing merrily with its tail till it saw my wife, when it promptly lay down, started mewing pitiably and played orphan. Next the melts, the diamonds, the lot. Pussy was carried home tenderly and offered a saucer of milk – which she refused to touch. She looked, she sniffed, but touch it she wouldn't.

The little woman was awfully worried: she hadn't picked Pussy out of the gutter to have her starve to death in our kitchen, had she? Something had to be done fast. We racked our brains and then, on the verge of despair, hit on the brilliant idea that of course, Pussy was too young to eat, she had to be fed from a baby-bottle.

That was easy, because we just then happened to have a

baby in the house too – our second son, Amir – and it followed that we had at least a dozen bottles in the fridge, all sterilized and ready for use.

"Are you crazy?" said the woman, "Feed a filthy cat from Amir's bottle? You go to the pharmacy and buy another bottle for Pussy."

"Not me," I said, "I'll look like a bloody fool."

I would too. I mean, a grown man, very respectable-looking and that, coming into a pharmacy and saying, "May I have a baby-bottle for a cat?" I'd sound like a freak or something. On my way to the pharmacy I therefore resolved to hush up the bottle's true purpose, and just casually told our friendly neighbourhood pharmacist:

"One baby-bottle, please."

"How's Amir then?" she asked.

"Thanks. Weighs over 12 pounds already."

"Fancy that! Well, and what sort of bottle shall it be?"

"The cheapest . . ."

An ominous silence fell on the pharmacy. The other customers drew away from me in disgust, "Tsk-tsk," said their glances, "A well-dressed fellow like that, wears glasses, drives a big car – and for his little baby he buys the cheapest bottle. Bah!"

The kindly smile on the pharmacist's face vanished as well:

"Suit yourself," she said, "Though these cheap bottles burst in no time."

"Never mind," I muttered, "I'll glue it."

The pharmacist shrugged and produced a large array of bottles, ranging from burst-proof, jet-age, made-in-Britain miracles, to a miserable brownish affair that would make any decent infant puke.

"That one," I said with downcast eyes, "The brown."

At this point a fat lady standing next to me intervened. "Look, mister," she said, "I know it's none of my business, but still. Your baby is the most precious thing you have, right? So what I say is: save on anything else, if you must, but always buy the best for your child. I am speaking as a

55

mother, sir!"

She was fat and I didn't like her. I asked about prices. The super-bottles cost anywhere between 35 and 62 pounds, the brown wretch was only 7.20.

"He breaks them all anyway," I whispered, "It'd be a waste of money to buy the expensive sort."

"Why should he break them?" the pharmacist said, "If you hold him like this, see, with his head in the crook of your left arm, there's no way for him to break anything." I could just picture a bediapered Pussy reclining against my left arm. What the hell.

"He's sort of restless, our baby," I explained, "He kicks. So may I have the brown, please? . . ."

"I guess you don't feed him right, then," said the fat mother, "Have you got a nurse for him?"

"No . . . I mean . . ."

"I'll send you one," she said, "A restless baby needs professional care. Wait, I'll give her a call right now and see if she's free."

There were less than three yards between me and the door, and if it hadn't been for those two big fellows standing there like so many rocks of Gibraltar, I'd have made a dash for it. Let Pussy hunt mice, dammit.

"You sure ought to be grateful to the lady," the pharmacist told me, "She's got four of her own, and they're the nicest, quietest babies you've ever seen. She'll get you a first-class nurse and your little Amir will soon be cured of his bad habits."

Amir is a perfectly serene and quiet baby, mind you. He just lies on his back all day and only very occasionally comments: Glo-glo.

I still had a flicker of hope that the nurse would be out, but she was in.

"She could come and see you tomorrow," Fat Mama said, "Would eleven o'clock be all right?"

"No," I said, "We'll be busy then."

"One o'clock?"

"That's when I have my fencing lesson."

"And your wife?"

"She too."

"One-thirty then."

"We'll be sleeping."

"Four?"

"Still sleeping."

"Six?"

"We're having guests."

"Eight?"

"Going to the museum."

"Listen!" Mama hissed at me, "Just seeing her won't cost you anything, if that's what's worrying you!"

The other customers seemed ready to strangle me with their bare hands. They shouldn't allow monsters like that to have babies, said their looks. Ma herself slammed the receiver and turned her back on me. The pharmacist asked coldly: "The cheapest then, is it?"

I just nodded my head, quite beyond speech. Only let me get out of here alive, I vowed, and I'll open a cat orphanage.

The pharmacist gave me a glance full of loathing and made a final attempt: "Look at this flimsy rubber nipple," she said, "Before you know it the hole will have gotten so large that Baby may God forbid choke . . ."

By then I knew nothing any more except for the pounding in my head.

"No matter," I snarled, "We'll make another baby."

That was the last straw. A middle-aged gentleman approached me, shaking a fist in my face: "Listen," he shouted, "I don't know who the devil you are, but let me just ask you this: do you know what they make these cheap bottles for? They make them for feeding the cat!" I felt my knees go weak. There's a limit to what a man can stand.

"All right," I said hoarsely, "Give me the best . . ."

"Sixty-two pounds, please," announced the pharmacist, and everybody breathed with relief. The bottle I'd got was the British superstar, jet-age and burst-proof, and complete with feeding-chart and two-year warranty.

The wife threw a fit when she saw it. "What's the matter with you?" she said, "Why did you have to pick the most expensive bottle in the shop?"

"Woman," I replied, "I'll save on anything you like, but not on kittens!"

Come to think of it, who said a cat will eat out of a baby-bottle? What is it — a baby?

Standing Orders

I trust my readers know by now that I generally avoid writing about my own little family. I mean, why should anyone care that our wonderful Rafi's baby brother Amir is a delightful child, a sight smarter than your baby, dear reader; that he's a particularly handsome child, red hair and all; and that at the age of seven months, when most babies can't even crawl yet, he, Amir, already cried because he couldn't either. Well, as I said, all this is very thrilling, but it certainly doesn't concern anyone except the family and a few close friends.

Still, for all that I've been saying, something happened the other day which I feel I must not keep silent about.

Amir stood.

The point isn't that he stood. Every baby learns to stand sooner or later. But he, Amir, *stood!* It happened quite suddenly too. At 5.10 in the afternoon we all of a sudden hear a wildly exultant cry from his room, we rush over and — by golly! — the child is holding on to the bars of his cot and he's standing right up on his feet like a man. "Attaboy!" we cheered him, "That's great, Amir! Bravo! Do it again!"

But doing it again he can't. He's learnt very fast — that's to say, fairly on time — or at any rate not very much later than other kids his age — how to pull himself up to a standing position, but sitting down again is beyond him. And as he obviously can't stand on his feet all day, my son calls loudly for someone to come and help him down. He sure likes to stand, though, does Amir. He's mad about standing. Some fifty times a day, therefore, he raises the alarm:

"Dad-dy! Dad-dy!"

He calls me to come to his rescue — *me*, his father, his tower of strength. It's moving, that's what it is. His mother, my wife, flutters about him all day with food and pootshie-mootshie, whereas I, having to work for a living, hardly ever see him. And yet the child, with this marvellous instinct of his, nevertheless feels, *knows,* who it is he can *really* trust around here. So whenever he gets up and can't get down again, he cries:

"Dad-dy! Dad-dy!"

And Daddy comes. No matter *what* I'm doing — eating, shaving, taking a phone call — when my son calls I drop everything and rush to his side. It's hard on the little woman, I know, it's a blow to her self-esteem. Even I am a bit embarrassed that her child should so obviously prefer me. Fortunately, she's a sensible girl and does her best not to show she's jealous. Each time Amir gives me the old heave-ho she says generously:

"It's all right, Ephraim, don't mind me. He loves *you*, and that's all there is to it."

The only flaw in this arrangement is that a man's got to get some sleep.

As long as my little honey-chile only needed settling down by day, I would go and detach him from the bar without complaint, but when he started knocking me up in the wee hours I got a bit nervy. Me, I need at least three hours' sleep at night or I stutter. The little wretch stood his ground, though. One long day's night I rolled out of bed some 30 times in answer to the stand-or-fall cry of "Dad-dy!"

The woman would sleep soundly through it all, with just an occasional smile of sympathy on her lips as she dreamt I'd got up again. I wasn't angry with her: my boy was calling *me*, after all, not her. All the same, it was rather infuriating that I, a hard-working male, should have to rush back and forth between my bed and the all-night stand of that little pest, while there, right beside me, a mother, an expert, a *pro*, dammit, lies sleeping all serene. Amir himself wasn't playing

60

fair either, I must say. To begin with, he could easily have learnt to sit down by himself already like any other normal kid his age. In the second place, it's no way to behave to one's own flesh-and-blood mummy, ignoring her like that. It's positively offensive. He's got red hair, this child has.

"Amir," I therefore said to him one day when the wife had gone off to the hairdresser's, "You don't always have to shout 'Daddy!' Shout 'Mummy!' 'Mummy' — d'you hear? — Mummy! Mummy! Mummy! Mummy! Mummy! Mummy! Mu-u-u-m-m-y-y-y-y-y-y!'"

Amir's a fast learner, and my wife spends a lot of time at the hairdresser's. I'll never forget the night when the demand for settlement came loud and clear as:

"Mum-my! Mum-my!"

I shook the little woman:

"Darling," I whispered, "Your son is up!"

The wife listened hard, got the message, and slipped out of bed, a trace of panic in her eyes. As she returned, she threw me a nasty look but said nothing.

"Better stay on your toes," I whispered with feeling, "He may call again."

And he did. All that week I slept like a log, while the little woman turned into a nervous wreck. Our up-the-down baby had learnt the true meaning of motherhood. He'd learnt what mothers are *for,* I mean. She got up every night and all night. I counted once, and it was 40 times. Ah, well, life isn't all jam.

"I'm truly glad the child has gone back to you," I told her, "It's more natural, sort of."

"Yeah."

My holiday came to an end one night at four a.m. "Ephraim," thus the woman, "You're wanted."

I turn to listen, and there's no mistaking it:

"Dad-dy! Dad-dy!"

So the ball is back in my court. Amir stands up for me again, and I suspect dark doings but say nothing. I just settle and resettle the little upstart, and the woman's eyes are

61

brighter than a thousand suns. I'm willing to bet that whenever I'm out of the house she sneaks over to the bar and drills the child:

"Daddy! Daddy! Da-a-ad-dy-y-y-y-y!"

No wonder our little bar-tender is confused at the moment, though sooner or later he'll have to make up his mind all the same. It's his mother or me — one of us will have to go. To the bar, that is, to detach him.

What to Buy Teacher

I am lying on my bed, fully dressed. The light is on over my head and under my feet are the morning papers. My brain is racing. The little woman sits in front of the mirror and applies bioplacenta cream to her face in order to rejuvenate the cells of her skin. This is the hour of truth for artists my age. I've been going around with my problem for weeks and I can be silent no longer. I must talk it over with someone: what I do now will decide my fate for the next ten years. What does a man marry his wife for anyway?

"Darling," I say hoarsely, "I must tell you something, and please don't get upset or jump to conclusions. I've felt this coming for a long time. The point is — I think I've come to a dead end in my writing. It's worse than just writer's block. It's a creative impasse. I've been thinking to maybe give up writing altogether. Or at least for a year or two. I'm all drained. I need a rest . . ."

The wife applies bioplacenta and keeps silent.

"Do you think I'm right?" I ask anxiously, "Tell me honestly: do you think I'm right?"

The woman turns to stare at me. I'm on tenterhooks.

"Ephraim," she says at last, "We've got to buy Rafi's kindergarten teacher something."

"When?"

"She's leaving at the end of the week. Her husband got transferred to Beersheba, We've got to buy her some present."

I've a feeling her answer isn't relevant.

"Tell me," I say in a slightly raised voice, "Why can't you

listen when I talk to you?"

"I do listen," says the wife, starting on a new layer of the salmon-pink stuff, "I remember every word you said."

"What did I say?"

"Tell me why don't you listen when I talk to you."

"Right. Then why don't you answer?"

"Because I'm thinking, that's why."

Hm, well, I admit my problem isn't easy. "Do you think," I say, "that I ought to somehow make an intellectual effort to overcome my temporary lassitude?"

The little one doesn't answer.

"Are you listening?"

"Of course I'm listening. I'm not deaf. An intellectual effort to overcome your temporary whatsit."

"So?"

"A box of chocolates."

"What?"

"A box of chocolates. Not too expensive, and always welcome as a present, don't you think?"

"Yes," I agree at once, "But that doesn't solve my problem, dear. If I do stop working for a year or two — what then? How do I fill the spiritual void, I mean?"

The wife slaps her face lightly with her eyes on me. The eyes say kindergarten teacher.

"Are you listening at all?"

"Don't keep asking me that. The spiritual void I mean." She remembers every word.

"I figured," I say, "that I might do a bit of painting or music to start with."

"Why not?"

"And in time I might take up alligator yoga."

"Uh-huh."

She takes a piece of tissue and rubs off the bioplacenta with raised eyebrows.

"Anyhow," she mumbles, "one's got to think of everything."

I have nothing to say to that, so I say nothing.

"Ephraim," thus the wife, "Why don't you say something?"

"I'm thinking. I'm thinking if it wouldn't be a good idea to cut up the maid and pack the pieces in a green suitcase."

The little one is deep in her own thoughts. She's leafing casually through a women's magazine too.

"Are you listening?"

"Pack the maid in a green suitcase."

Every word. She does something to her eyebrows with a little brush, and she's turned on the radio as well. Sinatra. I give my thoughts free reign, "We could buy Teacher a baby zebra on the cheap."

Even that doesn't work. No spark.

"Yes," the little one says, massaging her throat base-to-chin, "Fine."

"In that case," I sum up the evening's discussion, "I'll go see my mistress and spend the night with her. Listening?"

"You'll spend the night with her."

"So?"

"I think flowers might be best after all."

She gets up and moves to the bathroom to wash off the salmon, and I'm left alone with my racing brain. Seems I'll have to go on writing for the present. Yes, but what'll we buy Teacher?

Still Life with Goats

The day had started like any other. The weather was fair, the sea was calm, Amir was quiet. It looked as though nothing would happen, and then at noon a lorry pulled up in front of the house and Morris, an uncle of ours on the woman's side, appeared on the doorstep.

"I heard how you'd moved to a new flat," Uncle Morris said, "So I brought you this oil painting."

He motioned for the two burly porters waiting outside to carry it up. We were truly moved. Old Morris is the pride of my wife's family: he's rich, and he cuts some ice with people who cut some ice. He *was* a bit late with his present — two-and-a-half years in fact, but who's counting.

The picture itself was a two-by-two-yard affair in a rococo-baroque gilded frame, and its theme was Jewish custom, tradition, and milieu. The right side showed a typical Jewish street in a ghetto or a nightmare, with lots of sky and pink clouds. On top was a lifesize sun, at bottom goats and cows (two by two!). Then there was a road with a rabbi carrying the Scrolls of the Law, followed by a number of young Talmudic scholars and a boy of thirteen visibly preparing for his *barmitzvah*. The background had a windmill, a couple of fiddlers, a roof, a moon, a wedding, and everybody's mother washing clothes in the river. On the far left there was an ocean with a fishing-net and a sailboat, in the middle distance some birds and New York, America. The whole was executed in bright Technicolor. It was the ghastliest thing we had ever seen, in or out of a picture frame.

"Wow!" we said to Morris, "But really, you shouldn't have."

"Aw," thus Morris, "I'm an old man, I can't take it all to the grave with me . . ."

After my wife's uncle had gone we collapsed in front of the atrocity and felt as wretched as the Jews in it. It seemed as if our whole flat was acrawl with goats, clouds, and minuscule Talmudic scholars. We looked for the criminal's signature underneath, but he'd wisely left it vague. I was in favour of burning the horror then and there, but the little woman said didn't I know what old people were like, one couldn't hurt their feelings like that, Uncle Morris would never forgive us. Burning was out. All the same, we knew we'd die if anyone ever saw us with it, so I dragged it out to the balcony and left it there, business side to the wall.

* * *

Next we forgot all about it. That's one nice thing about the human mind: its ability to forget practically everything. From *behind*, the picture didn't look so terrible anyhow, the more as one of our climbers had instinctively begun to grow over it.

All was well, except that once in a while the little woman would sit up in bed suddenly and whisper: "What if Morris should come to see us, though?"

"He won't," I'd say sleepily, "Why should he?"

* * *

He did.

May I never have to go through another experience like that. We were having lunch, and we'd just got to the sweet when the doorbell went. I got up to open and in came Morris. The picture was sleeping on the balcony with its face to the wall, the woman was spooning up her icecream all unawares, and here was Uncle Morris.

"How are you?" he asked benignly, and moved on to his doom. I did briefly consider escape, but then the wife's shocked face appeared round the door and she said:

"Sorry, Uncle, the living room's a mess . . . Just stay here a

67

minute talking to Ephraim while I fix it . . .''

We stayed in the passage and talked to Ephraim, while from the room came heavy steps, then the little woman herself passed us and returned with the ladder, then a sound as if the ceiling had caved in (two by two!), and finally her voice from the scene of the crime, calling for us to come in.

We did. The little woman was lying half dead on the couch, but Uncle's present was up. Not hanging quite straight, but up. Covering half the window, two smaller pictures and a cuckoo-clock, but definitely up and still slightly swaying.

Uncle Morris was surprised and pleased to see his picture there, but pointed out it needed a little more light, didn't we think? We said yes, and could he please let us know beforehand next time he meant to come, we'd like to receive him properly.

"Rubbish," said Morris, "What's an old man like me want? A cup of tea? A piece of cake? . . ."

Little did he know. We, anyhow, decided we'd better be ready with his piece of cake next time. From time to time we'd hold a surprise exercise. We'd be in bed, say, and suddenly the woman would shout, "Morris!" I'd leap for the balcony, the woman'd sweep everything off the wall, I'd leap back and — heigh-ho, up she goes! We called it "Operation Mussolini" (hanging's too good for it). After two weeks of intensive drill we were down to 90 seconds, getting rid of the ladder and all — an athleto-artistic feat if ever there was one.

On that disastrous Saturday when Morris phoned to say would it be all right if he came that evening, we therefore said yes with great enthusiasm. Now we'd have time to prepare.

We decided to really lay it on. I took two standing lamps, covered them with red, green, and yellow cellophane like in the theatre, and planted one on each side of the picture. The woman draped a huge flower garland round the gilded frame. In for a penny, in for a pound, as she said. Then we stood back smugly to admire the picture: a more sickening thing one couldn't imagine.

At six — the bell. The woman went gaily to let Uncle in while I, giggling a little to myself, trained my spotlights on the goats and the washing mothers.

Then the door opened and in came Dr. Perlmutter, Director-General of the Ministry of Education and Culture, accompanied by his wife.

* * *

I stood there in the limelight bang under the picture, while my wife was making herself invisible behind our distinguished visitors. Dr. Perlmutter is one of the grandest people we know, a man of taste and learning, and a great art connoisseur. His wife paints. They came in, looked, and shuddered. I moved a bit to try and at least keep the goats out of view . . .

"What a delightful surprise," said someone in my throat, "Do sit down, please."

Dr. Perlmutter polished his glasses and seemed incapable of speech. The flowers! If at least there hadn't been all those flowers round the frame!

"What a nice place you have here," Mrs. Perlmutter mumbled, "All these . . . uh . . . pictures . . ."

I could positively feel the young Talmudists dancing behind my back. For a while we just sat there on pins and needles, the eyes of our visitors staring at It. The wife had managed to "accidentally" trip over a wire, so that the spotlights were off now, but the picture was still fully lit from the rabbi's shoulders down. Dr. Perlmutter asked for a glass of water for his headache. My wife returned from the kitchen and slipped a note into my hand: "Ephraim! Use your head!"

"Sorry we just came by like this," Mrs. Perlmutter said at last, "My husband wanted to talk to you about a lecture tour in the U.S."

"Oh!" I cried, "When?"

"Never mind," said Dr. Perlmutter, "It's . . . it can wait . . ."

I realized we'd better offer some sort of explanation, or we'd be banished from civilized society forever. The wife took courage.

"You're probably wondering," she began, "what this

69

picture is doing here."

The Perlmutters looked up.

"Yes," they said, "What?"

* * *

Then Uncle Morris walked in. We performed the introductions. They took to him at once.

"You were going to tell us about this picture," Dr. Perlmutter reminded the little woman a few minutes later.

"Yes," she whispered, "Ephraim, please!"

I looked at my treacherous wife, then at the frozen Perlmutters, the scholars, the windmill, and lastly at our beaming Uncle Morris.

"A beautiful picture," I declared with lowered eyes, "So airy . . . the texture . . . the symbols . . . lots of water and . . . uh . . . oil . . . By the way, we got it from Uncle here!"

"Are you a collector, then?" Mrs. Perlmutter asked him.

"Mm . . . not this sort of thing, though," Morris answered, a charitable smile on his lips, "I go in for miniatures myself. But you know, madam — you won't mind me speaking frankly, my dears — young people today have such awful taste, I was sure they'd prefer this sort of monstrosity . . ."

"Not at all," said I, and picked up a pair of scissors, "We absolutely adore miniatures . . ."

And with that I put my scissors to the river and cut out three mothers and a cloud. Next came the boat with two fiddlers. I felt a surge of creative joy and, bubbling with laughter, stuck my blade into the fishing net and out came the rabbi. The mill got a Talmudist, the goats went to the wedding, and the cow jumped over the moon . . .

By the time I'd finished I was all alone with my wife again. A bit scared, but with evident relief, she began laying out my creations. There were 32 of them. We're starting an art gallery.

A la Recherche du Temps Perdu

The other day my wife says to me: "Listen, next Saturday they're having a '53 class reunion. All the old crowd'll be there. So if you feel like it, I mean, only if you really don't mind, it'd be nice if you came along." I said: "I won't know a soul there. I do mind. I don't feel like it. You go by yourself." She said: "I'm not going by myself. The least little thing I ask is too much for you . . ."

I came along. The crowd was in high spirits, like all crowds at all class reunions. The minute we entered everybody threw their arms round my wife and called her Poppy. Poppy! Me, I was as lonely and forlorn as Israel at the Security Council. The lively conversation skipped from one subject to the next, as the pleasant memories overcame them:

"Anybody heard about Tchachik? Is it true he flunked an S.O. course? I'm not surprised, he never was much of an intellect. How's Shoshka? I hear she's aged dreadfully. No, it's just that her second husband is 20 years younger than she is. Hey, remember that time she shinned up the drainpipe with Shtuckler on her heels? And the time she went bathing at Micky's by moonlight! Such a goose! . . ." They all shrieked with laughter.

"That's nothing!" the crowd went on, "That time Benny caught Minka making eyes at Kugler! Oh Lord! We thought we'd die laughing! Especially Sacha! Like when he of all people had to do the Charleston with Berger's ma! What an idiot! Remember how he sat down on the stove at Moskowitz's?"

I felt like a freak. I didn't know a soul there. I'm a graduate of the class of '48 of the Berzsenyi Daniel Realgimnazium, Budapest, myself. Any objections?

"Oo!" some woman screamed suddenly, "Guess who I met in Paris two years ago? Klachkes! They say he's selling postcards to tourists. He always used to be arty! Remember how he burnt his eyebrows?"

"Oh well," I said, "what else did you expect of Klachkes?"

"I don't know," said somebody. "He always wanted to be an architect, didn't he?"

"Don't be funny," I snickered, "Klachkes and architecture! I bet he's forgotten the ABC by now!"

That made them all laugh again. I regained my self-confidence.

"Is it true Yoske and Nina got married?" somebody asked, "You could've knocked me over — Yoske and *Nina! . . .*"

"Can you imagine what they must've looked like at the wedding?" I remarked, and had everyone in convulsions. "Oh, and remember that time Nina tried to dry her slip in the fridge? She always had a screw loose. And Yoske with his rabbits! I can never look at a cabbage without thinking of him!. . ."

I'd scored a hit! The crowd roared. From then on I never let the reins of the conversation slip out of my hands, as I kept raking up old memories far into the night. They were particularly delighted with my description of how Sacha sold his battered pick-up twice, and what Berger found in his bed after he'd filched Moskowitz's top-hat. When we were leaving, my wife said: "You were the life of the party. I never knew you had it in you!" I said: "Oh well, Poppy, you never used to be very bright."

Les Parents Terribles

We'd been debating the question for months: to go or not to go abroad. We'd weighed all the pros and cons, we'd searched our conscience, slept on it for nights on end, and decided: to go.

Once we'd made up our minds there was only one problem left: what would the children say? Well, there's Rafi — but Rafi is a big boy, you can already talk to him as to a grownup person. He's sure to understand how the King of Switzerland has invited Mummy and Daddy to come and visit him, and how you mustn't say no to a king because then he gets mad at you. So much for Rafi. That leaves Amir, who's only two-and-a-half years old, just the age when a child is most attached to his parents. What do we tell Amir?

A tough question. We'd heard of people leaving their little ones for a mere fortnight — with the most horrible consequences. One little girl in Jerusalem we know of was abandoned by her irresponsible parents for a month — to Yugoslavia *they went* — and she's been full of complexes since, and left-handed to boot.

We started discussing the question one day over lunch, but we'd no sooner exchanged our first few words in French, than Amir looked up from his plate with those big sad eyes of his and asked pathetically: "Why? *Why?* . . . "

No doubt the child had sensed something and got scared. He's very attached to us, is Amir. We looked at each other, the wife and I, and promptly gave up the whole idea. I mean, foreign lands are a dime a dozen, but how many children does a man have? Two. And one of them little. We're not going abroad and that's that. Try and make us. And anyhow, how can we possibly enjoy a place like Paris with always this nagging thought in our mind that back home Amir may perhaps be writing with his left hand already? Kids aren't something to be trifled with, mind you. Kids are a lifetime vocation, and if you aren't willing to make some sacrifice for them you may as well drop everything and go.

Exactly, That's just what we want to do. We're dying to go. We haven't been abroad in donkey's years. We want to go abroad.

But what do we do about Amir and his big sad eyes?

We went and talked to Mrs. Plim, a neighbour of ours whose husband is a pilot, so she gets free airline tickets twice a year. It turned out that what she does is — she always breaks the news *gradually*. She tells her kids all about the lovely places she and their daddy are going to see, and later they take pictures everywhere and bring them home to show the kids. The point is to make the child feel part of it all, to make him feel as if he himself had been on that trip with Mummy and Daddy. A bit of tact, a little insight, that's all there is to it.

Good. We figured we might as well start on the insight at once, so at home I took Amir on my knees and said:

"Do you know, my boy, that there are *such* high mountains in the world that . . ."

"Not go-way!" screamed Amir, "Not go-way! Amir not stay allolone! Amir Daddy-Mummy! Not mountains! Not go-way! Not go-way! . . ."

His blue eyes were streaming with tears and he clung to me trembling as a little leaf.

"We're not going!" we cried, his mother and I, "We'll stay right here with Amir! Not go to the naughty-naughty mountains! Mummy-Daddy Amir forever! Not go-way! . . ."
To hell with abroad! All the lakes of Italy aren't worth one tear in the eyes of our sweet darling. One smile of his is more precious to us than all the sunsets in the world. We're staying! Maybe when the child's a bit older, eighteen perhaps, or

74

twenty, maybe then we'll go abroad. For now let's just forget about it.

The matter would have ended there, except that now a new problem cropped up, to wit: next morning we decided to go abroad anyway. We love our Amir very much, but we also love going abroad, and that's the truth. So what do we do about the little fellow now?

We resolved on action. We know this woman who's something of a child psychiatrist, so we went and put the problem to her.

"You've handled this badly, I must say," the psychiatrist told us, "Don't you know you should never lie to a child? There's an innocence about children which only responds to the truth. You must be open with him. Open and honest. Like, for instance, don't go about your packing behind his back. Do it openly, let him watch, and then he won't suspect you of trying to run away on him . . ."

At home we took down two of our largest suitcases and brought Amir in to watch.

"Amir," we told him all open and honest, "Mummy and Daddy . . ."

"Not go-way!" Amir broke out, "Not go-way! Amir loves Mummy-Daddy! Amir not allolone! Not go-way! . . ."

He was positively shaking, his eyes all wet, his little nose all crimson, his arms flailing in helpless panic. Oh, God, how could we do this to him? We took him in our arms and hugged him close. "We're not going!" we swore, "Who said we were going? We just fetched these suitcases down to see if there were any toys for Amir in them! Mummy and Daddy are staying home, you hear! For ever! Only here! Always here! Only Amir! Never anything but Amir! Abroad naughty!"

But this time the shock has evidently been too much for him. Our boy is sobbing as if his little heart would break.

He is holding on to my trouser legs like he'll never let go again. Oh, my poor baby, what have we done to you?

"Don't just stand there," the little woman cries in consternation, "Get him some bubblegum!"

75

Amir's weeping stops with a squeal of brakes.

"Bubblegum?" he says, "Daddy bring Amir bubblegum from the broad?"

"Yes," I say quickly, "With stripes!"

The child gets up, the child isn't crying, the child is happy. "Bubblegum-with-stripes! Bubblegum-with-stripes!" he sings, dancing about the room and clapping his hands, "Go-way, Daddy, go-way, Mummy, go broad! Bring Amir *heaps* of bubblegum!"

His eyes shine, his cheeks glow, the child is overjoyed.

"Go-way!" he shouts, "Go-way *now!* Go broad! Why Mummy-Daddy not go? Go-ho-ho! . . ."

There, now he's crying again. His big blue eyes are wet with tears, his whole little body is trembling. He drags the suitcases over and dumps them under our noses.

"We'll go in a little while," we promise, "In a little while soon."

"No! *Now!*"

So that's why we left for Europe a week earlier than planned. The last few days were particularly hard because the child kept urging us to be gone, to be gone already. Every morning he'd wake up and be disappointed all over again to find us still there. He's very attached to us, is the child. We intend to bring him lots of bubblegum with stripes. We'll bring the psychiatrist some too.

Their Finest Shower

Uri Geller has been and gone, and it looks as if we still don't know for sure: *is* there such a thing as ESP or *isn't* there? What I do know is that whether there is or isn't, I've got it.

I'm telepathic, that's what. My powers haven't been turned to account by anyone in show biz yet, because they're revealed at home, along a strictly defined path between my desk and the bathroom. It's something to do with numbers. The way it works is this: I go to the bathroom to take a shower. As soon as I start soaping my back — and this is the sober truth — at that very instant the phone rings. Always. My back: the telephone.

Actually it's been that way for years and I'm quite used to it by now, so what I do is — at a certain point in the soaping process I simply stop and wait for the ring. And it comes. It never fails. I can ignore it of course, pretend I've heard nothing, what with the swish of water and all. Or, again, I can tell myself: "Let's say I'm not home, huh?" But that's cheating because I *am* home, right? All that hot water sets the imagination soaring too. Me, I always picture a fat man with a cigar who sits there at the other end of the line in New York and wants to turn my latest into a great musical hit on Broadway.

So I take the call. I must. I rinse the soap off in a panic, gird my loins with a wet towel, and sprint through all those rooms with their wide-open windows till I reach the phone and the ringing stops. Or else someone says at the other end: "Hallo, is Davy there?" "What Davy?" I ask, so he hangs up, and all that's left of him is a wet stain on the carpet.

Back to the shower. I drop the wet towel — sneeze — get in under the warm water again, start soaping my back and the phone rings. Now there are two possibilities: if I *don't* go it's the fat musical with the cigar; if I *do* it's Davy.

Telephokinesis. Moving people about by soap.

* * *

The little woman says it's rubbish, she doesn't see what's telepathic about it. Nobody rings because I'm taking a shower, it's the other way round: me, I sense that someone's about to ring me, so I start soaping. It does sort of work both ways, in fact. Take the night of November 17 last, when I was on pins and needles and that fateful call from London wouldn't come. I sat there fretting for hours, working myself into a stew, till about midnight the wife took pity on me.

"Know what?" she said, "Try the shower . . . maybe after all . . ."

What could I lose? I stripped and turned on the hot water (cold isn't much of a telepathic lead), and soaped myself carefully. I get to my back . . .

London.

I guess I'm a good medium. Sometimes I happen to find myself on the other side of the fence. I feel this sudden urge to phone somebody and I don't know why. I move to the phone like a sleepwalker and dial:

"Is Ronny home?"

"Yes, but he's in the shower."

Telephokinesis. I feel a sort of current the minute Ronny starts soaping his back. It's eerie. And the craziest part of it is — it's not the shower itself that sets up the current, it's not just the soaping either. It's the *back* that does it. I tried it out, believe me: I soap my toes — silence. My chest — nothing. My back — prrr-prrr.

I mentioned the fact to some friends and they nearly all of them confirmed my hunch. It seems that when a really good medium gets in under the shower people all over the world sit up and for no good reason start dialling numbers at random. There's precious little you can do against it. The other day at the supermarket I spotted something with a label that said: "Soapless Soap". Aha, I told myself, that may be your solution. No soap — no telephokinesis! The blow came when I tried it. I reached my back, and the ringing followed as the night the day. It turns out that it isn't the soap that counts, it's the soaping.

* * *

So I'm telepathic. I've considered letting the whiz-kids test me, but I'm afraid of the publicity — nosy reporters, all that. I've trouble enough as it is. Only yesterday I had a phone call from one of those sceptics who deny the existence of Soap Telepathy altogether.

"Listen, buddy," the fellow sneered, "For your information: I've been soaping my back for the past 15 minutes and the phone hasn't rung once!"

"Warm water?"

"Hot! And I changed soap twice."

"Maybe your phone is out of order . . ."

"Yeah? I'm calling you on it, aren't I? So where's your telepathy?"

"Dunno," I said sadly and wiped the soap off the receiver and returned to my shower.

Will He, Won't He

If you see two people on our block arguing these days, you can bet your life that their topic is: Will Amir Kishon go to kindergarten or won't he? The betting is 3:1 in favour of "won't" and Amir, to be sure, stays at home.

It wasn't always like that. When we first brought him to that nice kindergarten round the corner, he took to it like a duck to water. He joined the crowd, wove plastic mats with the best of them, and rung-a-ring o'roses like the tyro he was. By next morning, though, he knew the score:

"I won't go to kindergarten!" he yelled, "Mummy-Daddy, not kindergarten! I won't! I won't! I won't! . . ."

We asked why not kindergarten, you loved it, didn't you? But Amir gave no reasons, he just wouldn't go, he'd sooner emigrate, anything but go to kindergarten.

Our good neighbours the Seligs frowned heavily upon our meek surrender.

"Pooh," said Erna, "That's no way to handle a child of three. Don't plead with him. Just take him to his kindergarten and that's it!"

Ah, what a woman: firm, resolute, no nonsense about her. Too bad she has no children of her own. Deeply impressed, we bundled Amir up next morning and took him on a one-way trip to the kindergarten. Just left him there and went off, we did. He yelled, he kicked — we didn't care. We shook hands, his mother and I, very pleased with ourselves. He's crying? Let him! That's what he's got lungs for, what? Only much later, a minute, a minute-and-a-half, we nevertheless began to wonder: is he *still* crying? We rushed back and found our student standing by the gate and shaking it — or rather, himself — with might and main:

"Mum-my! Mum-my! . . ."

So power politics had failed. Violence begets violence.

About a week later we went to see the Birnboims who live on our street, a nice couple, nothing special but still, and conversation turned on kindergartens in general, and on the one particular garten our kinder refused to go to.

"He won't," we concluded, "he just won't."

"Of course he won't," said Mrs. Birnboim, who's a very cultured sort of woman, "He won't because you're trying to force him. He's not a puppy you can train. Look, take our Gaby. He refuses to go to kindergarten too, but the last thing we'd do is force him. We're waiting patiently till he himself asks us to take him there. If you don't, if you start on the wrong foot with kindergarten, your child may well end up hating school of any kind, he may take an aversion to learning *as such!* So no, we don't force him. It's a bit of a nuisance of course, but it's worth it."

We were green with envy.

"And it works, does it?"

"You bet it does!" thus our host, "From time to time we ask Gaby, casual-like, you know: 'Gaby, how about going to kindergarten tomorrow?' Just that. And if it's no — it's no. I'm positive that one day he'll come of his own accord and beg us to take him there."

Here Gaby stuck his head through the door:

"Daddy, come and tuck me in."

"Come, Gaby," said Mr. Birnboim, "Come in nicely and say hullo to our visitors. They've got a little boy at home just like you."

"Yeah," said Gaby, "Tuck me in, though."

"In a minute."

"Now!"

"First be a good boy and say hullo to our visitors."

I shook Gaby's hand. A nice boy, tall, well built, looking a bit like Jack Nicholson only perhaps a year or two older. He needed a shave, did Gaby.

"Excuse me just a moment . . ." Birnboim got up for the tucking-in.

"Gaby," said Mrs. Birnboim casual-like, "You want to go to kindergarten tomorrow?"

"Nope."

"As you wish, darling. Nighty-night . . ."

"Actually I don't mind his not going," Mrs. Birnboim confessed when father and son had left the room, "He's due to join the Army next year anyway, he wouldn't really be happy among those toddlers . . ."

We left the Birnboims in a pensive mood. We agreed with their tactics on the whole, but the end-result didn't seem quite satisfactory. Anyhow, we said to ourselves, this entire kindergarten business is being more trouble than it's worth. Who says a child has to go to kindergarten in the first place? Did *I* go to kindergarten when I was little? I did, but so what? Maybe we'd better drop the whole idea?

Our family doctor gave us the final push when he said:

"It's pretty risky sending a child to kindergarten right now. There's a flu epidemic on, and they all catch it from each other . . ."

With a sigh of relief we summoned our student:

"Amir," we told him, "You're in luck. The doctor says you aren't to go to kindergarten because there's all kinds of nasty diseases there. So no more kindergarten for you! . . ."

And that's the end of the kindergarten problem. Amir goes every morning and spends all his time waiting for the microbes. Wild horses couldn't drag him away from there. Whenever our admirers ask how we managed it, we just lift an eyebrow and say airily:

"By medical means."

Summertime with Ants

A groundfloor flat has one advantage and one drawback. The advantage is that you don't have to climb stairs, the drawback is that the ants don't either. Each morning, therefore, a procession of ants crosses our doorstep, crawls up the wall near the bread-drawer and enters the sink. Soon there's a constant flow of back-and-forth traffic, the wee beasties carrying off whatever comes their way with manic zeal.

They say it's a common groundfloor phenomenon, and that this is a particularly anty summer. Be that as it may, my wife resolved upon fatal measures that very first morning:

"There's no point in just killing off a few," argued the little one, "We've got to find their nest!"

We traced the procession backwards. It led from our doorstep to the garden, disappeared temporarily under the hedge, popped up again a short way beyond, and from there ran north with various zigzags, over and underground. We came to a halt at the outskirts of town.

"Good Lord," said the wife, "they come from abroad!" Why had they made straight for us? What the hell's so special about our sink? Those are questions only the Queen Ant can answer. The labouring masses are awfully trade-unionized creatures who ask no questions but just carry off the load.

Still, the little woman considered their ways and got wise to them. She bought a box of anti-ant powder and scattered the deadly poison all along the trail from door to sink, and next morning the ants made very slow progress because they had all those powder hills to climb. They suffered no other ill effects. As a next step we went for them with the insect spray: the frontline troops succumbed; the main body marched sinkwards undaunted . . . "They've got guts, you've got to hand it to them," said the woman and washed the whole kitchen with kerosene, and the ants stayed away for two days, and so did we. At the end of this brief holiday the ant procession reappeared in force, and even seemed slightly more active than before. They discovered the cough syrup and went on a binge, and never gave another cough. The little woman abandoned her principles and went over to individual treatment, that is, just killing them off by the thousands every morning.

"It's no good," she said at last, "they're like the Chinese . . ."

Then came the salad days. The little woman heard somewhere that ants can't stand the smell of cucumbers, and at once laid out the entire contents of our salad bowl along their regular route. It soon transpired, though, that the ants themselves hadn't heard the news: they passed over the sliced cucumber with a sniff, and a few even sort of giggled outright.

Then we applied to the Sanitation Department and begged for guidance:

"What'll we do?" we asked.

"Nothing," said the doorman, "I've got ants in the kitchen myself."

Since then we've given up the struggle. We have breakfast and the procession passes the bread-drawer and makes for the sink. It's quite a part of the domestic scene by now. Each morning we check to see if everything's all right. The ants know us already and wave with a kind of reserved amiability, as between two adversaries of long standing who've learnt to respect each other in honourable combat. A worthy example of peaceful coexistence.

Madame Récamier Against the World

It all started with Hasya.

Hasya is a friend of the little woman's and she's mad about antiques — real ones, I mean, not that boring archaeological stuff from before B.C. One dark day Hasya took the little one window-shopping, and the wife came home in a tizzy and kicked our Danish coffee-table.

"Ugh!" she said, "Bah! These modern things can't begin to compare with antiques. I'm going to buy nothing but antique furniture from now on."

"Furniture?" I said, "What the hell for?"

"For atmosphere!"

She hadn't come back empty-handed from her window-shopping either. She'd bought a silver candlestick made of pure tin, and announced that henceforth we were to dine by candle-light every Friday evening. For atmosphere, I presume.

The day after she went off with Hasya again and returned with a scratchy wicker chair which, as far as I could see, would be useful for getting rid of unwelcome guests and for nothing else. This, it turned out, was "an original piece of rustic", to quote Hasya, and a real find. I asked the woman what we wanted it for.

"To look at. Or maybe I'll make it over into a dressing-table."

She had bought the anti-chair at Wexler's, and the next thing I learnt was that there are only three genuine antiquarians in this country altogether. There's Wexler himself, there's Joseph Aziz, and there's young Bendor who's also an expert restorer, that is, he makes new furniture look as good as old. These, the Big Three, rule supreme over the 28 antiques in circulation, which are passed from hand to hand, from dealer to dealer, in an endless round. The point is that Israel, rich as it is in archaeology, is lamentably poor in antiques. It so happens that neither European refugees nor Moroccan immigrants came here with Louis Seize or even Quinze cabinets in their luggage. It follows that when some scrap of Biedermeier or chip of Dresden does surface somewhere, all the people in the trade know about it. Like the famous Florentine chiffonier of Nahariya . . .

"All my friends are dying to get that chiffonier," the little one told me with glittering eyes, "They're asking 12,000 pounds for it, but the dealers think they'll come down."

"And the friends?"

"They don't know the address."

For that's the key to the whole industry: the address. You have an address — you have an antique; you haven't — you may whistle for the wind. Your true dealer will therefore sooner die than give away a name, a street, a number . . .

We'll never for instance know the identity of the previous owner of our Venetian grandfather clock (1873), which shows the position of the moon as well, never mind that for the past half century it's been fixed unwaveringly on a lunar eclipse. Maybe it'll make a nice dressing-table. The little one's friends are impressed by it anyhow, though some prefer the gilded crystal cage — 1900 and fit for an eagle. We got it cheap from young Bendor the Restorer, who bought it off a new immigrant from Kenya, who had sold it to Aziz through Wexler. Aziz also managed to lay hands upon one leg of an original Queen Anne table for my wife. It's a stunning leg: it has all these flowers and snakes curling round it, and it weighs a ton.

"Woman," I demanded after the porters had left, "This leg doesn't have a table to stand on. What did you buy it for?"

She'd bought it, she said, in anticipation. She was hoping that Aziz would rustle up some more legs for her, and then, when she had enough, they'd make a perfect support for something and she might even consider making them into a — right!

All in all, our flat is filling up. You can hardly move around in it these days without tripping over some piece of atmosphere or other. It's making us both restless. The little one has even started talking in her sleep, and from what I hear I gather she dreams of the Nahariyan-Florentine chiffonier every night . . .

* * *

The straw that broke my back, however, was the Biedermeier chest (1831).

By that time I'd already grown extremely sensitive to the sound of heavy steps on the staircase, and on this occasion they appeared ominously loud. Sure enough, the chest of drawers that came with them looked like a tombstone and weighed twice as much. Aziz or whoever had thrown in Field Marshal von Hindenburg's camp-bed (1918) by way of extra.

"I'm not a bloody field marshal," I roared, "and I'm not going camping! And what's the chest for?"

"For by my bed."

"And what about *my* bed?"

She always buys only one of everything. *One* chair, *one* candlestick, *one* leg.

"I'm sorry," the little one said contritely, "I'll ask them to get me everything in pairs from now on . . ."

Next morning I went to see Wexler.

I found the man busily tidying up his shop, that's to say throwing all his antiques higgledy-piggledy in a heap since — as he explained — the worse the chaos in Ye Olde, the greater the find when you find it.

As I waited for Wexler to finish his disarrangements, a map of the country with some dozen little coloured flags stuck in it here and there caught my eye. I went closer and saw that the flags bore legends like: "Vict. Footst.", "Span. Gobel.", and, somewhere near Haifa, "Floren. chiff." North Tel Aviv had a black (!) flag reading: "New site: Bied. chest, Gramp clock, E. cage, Hind. bed . . ."

The blood froze in my veins: the black flag was *us!*

I turned to Wexler and introduced myself as Alex Arunter because you never know, but Wexler just glanced at me, checked one of his files, then asked with a grin:

"And how's our Queen Anne leg today?"

"Fine," I said, blushing, "Bit lonely."

"I know. And your wife?"

"All right. I'd rather she didn't find me here, though. Are you expecting her?"

Wexler crossed over to his teleprinter and read the message aloud: "Madame Récamier at Aziz. Wants spinning-wheel. Over and out."

"She'll go to Bendor next because he may have the address of a spinning-wheel," Wexler calculated, "So we have about 45 minutes till she gets here. Now then, what can I do for you?"

"Mr. Wexler," I said, "I'm liquidating."

"Mm," said Wexler, "Well, yes, it doesn't do to hold on to antiques for too long. I hope you've told no one else?"

"No, just you."

At this point the phone on his desk rang. Wexler listened, then walked to the map and transferred the spinning-wheel flag to North Tel Aviv, La Récamier had just bought it. Operation Antitique went off smoothly.

Wexler got in touch with Bendor and informed him of the site closure. Bendor turned him over to Aziz, who had just acquired a new customer — some dippy South American millionaire. The little woman left the house at 12 to go window-shopping, and at 12:30 Wexler appeared with three deaf-and-dumb porters who took the whole antiqua-boodle off to young Bendor.

By 1 o'clock I was alone in the house. I lay down on our sofa (1967) and burst into song — the atmospheric pressure was off at last!

Or was it? At 1.30 I heard heavy steps outside and rushed to the door in alarm. Yes . . . there they were all coming back again . . . the rustic . . . the Queen Anne . . . the spinning-wheel . . . the lot . . .

"Ephraim!" I heard the jubilant voice of my wife in the rear, "Look what I've found for you! The second Biedermeier chest! . . ."

But when she came in and discovered there was only one chest after all, Madame Recamier burst into tears:

"You sneaks, all of you," she sobbed, "Aziz said he'd got it off some dippy South American millionaire . . . All my savings blown . . . the nasty, dirty, double-dealing . . ."

I was good and angry myself. I knew about the 28 items for ever rotating among the same customers, but that my own wife should buy out her own husband . . .

I took the little one in my arms:

"Know what?" I said, "Just because of what those crooks did to us, we'll go out now and buy the Florentine chiffonier of Nahariya!"

No one will ever know how we got hold of the address. Antique circles are buzzing with rumours. Hasya told us that Wexler suspects my little one hid in the Empire bureau in his shop one night, and overheard him discussing the chiffonier with his partner. Be that as it may, our household now boasts a 12,000-pound Florentine dressing-table, which has turned us in one blow into the foremost antiquarians of Israel. The teleprinters speak of no one but us. The Great Aziz himself was pleading with us the other day to sell him something, anything, because now that we've exploded the address myth, Hasya and co. have decided that they, too, can get along without the dealers.

Our possession of the Florentine chiffonier of North Tel Aviv, what's more, has completely upset the balance of power: out of the 28 antiques in the country — we have nine! Our refusal to sell has all but paralysed the market. Wexler and Aziz are at their wits' end. Only young Bendor manages somehow, because he's a restorer as well.

The Red Menace

Did I by any chance mention before that Amir's hair is sort of reddish? I did? Well, I'm making no secret of it. Me, I *like* red hair.

Maybe red doesn't quite describe it, though — he's positively scarlet, is Amir, his head looks like the original burning bush, like a cock's comb done by Chagall in his heyday. It doesn't bother me in the least, as I said, the more as it has its advantages too: if the child should get lost in a crowd, for instance, you'd find him easily because he sticks out a mile. So what? So he won't be a bullfighter. Who cares?

It's funny, though, because as far as I know there's never been a single redhead in all my family. Could be Amir is a direct descendant of King David, who was *"ruddy* and withal of a *beautiful countenance"*, so there! And anyhow, some of the greatest men in history were ginger, I don't remember all their names just now but I'm sure.

"To me," says the little woman, "Amir is the most beautiful child in the world!"

Truth to tell, Amir feels just the same about it. When he could hardly talk yet he'd already sit and gaze raptly in the mirror, and announce smugly:

"Amil gingel! Amil gingel!"

Positively delighted he was. We, his worldly-wise parents, knew that it wouldn't last, that as soon as he started nursery-school the other kids would gang up on him. Ah, my poor little redhead, what then?

We were right, of course, Amir hadn't been going to

nursery-school more than eight months when he came home in tears.

"This new boy," he wept, "He . . . he says . . . ginger . . ."

"He said you're ginger?"

"No . . . that he's *more* ginger . . ."

It's hard to understand him when he's crying. His teacher told us that a new student had turned up at nursery-school who was just as much of a redhead as Amir, and our boy resented the loss of his monopoly. We comforted him as best we could, and in less than five minutes he'd forgotten his sorrows and gone out to be afraid of cats. Only we, his parents, knew he was sitting on top of a seething volcano . . .

"He believes that being born a redhead is the best thing that can happen to a child," said my wife, "He's pleased, he's happy, but next year at kindergarten — what then?" She told me she has these nightmares in which her little Amir is running down the street as fast as his little legs will carry him, and a whole cohort (that's the sort of words she dreams, my wife), a whole cohort of kids are chasing him in a fire engine and yelling: "Gin-ger! Gin-ger!" Sometimes her pillow is wet with tears in the morning. A mother's heart is a sensitive thing: she eats too much supper in the evening, her heart suffers at night . . .

* * *

Then it happened. One day Amir came from kindergarten all excited:

"Daddy! Daddy!" he shouted, "D'you know what the kids called me? They called me carrot-head! That's what: carrot-head!"

"Did you punch them in the nose?"

"What for?"

He still hadn't realized that they were out to hurt his feelings. He thinks a carrot is something to eat, and carrot-head is some pretty sort of flower, and all day long he struts about like a peacock and sings: "Yippee, I'm a carrot-head! Yippee!"

My wife listens and her eyes fill with tears. The child isn't worried *yet,* he's happy and cheerful *now,* but one day the inevitable will happen, and he'll discover that redheadedness is a fate, a destiny. He is so utterly unprepared for it — it will break him . . .

"You are his father," my wife informed me, "You talk to him."

I took Amir on my knees:

"It's true you've got red hair, my boy," I said to him tenderly, "But you needn't feel bad about it. Nobody can help the colour of his hair, right? King David was a ginger and he beat Goliath all the same. So don't let them pester you because you're ginger, my poor love, but just tell them right to their face: Yes, I'm ginger, but my daddy isn't! . . ." Amir wasn't paying much attention, because he wanted to go out and throw stones at little dogs. He just babbled something about me, Daddy, not to be sad that I wasn't ginger, what mattered was that he, Amir, *was* a ginger, the most ginger in kindergarten, a carrot-head.

He sticks to his guns, the brat. These redheads are stubborn as hell, there's something positively annoying about them. Come to think of it, I'm not surprised they're persecuted, not surprised at all . . .

* * *

We left it at that for the time being, but we knew, his mother and I, that it wasn't the end. To be sure, a few days later we heard him crying outside, and when we rushed to his aid we found our tear-stained little boy sitting on a tricycle, and a gang of slightly older kids standing round menacingly.

I pushed my way through and hugged my baby:

"Who called you redhead?" I raged, "Which of you brats called my boy a redhead, ha?"

The gang blinked but said nothing. They could tell by my face that any one of them who so much as moved would be risking his life!

In the end Amir himself spoke up:

"Redhead nothing," he said, "I only took Nicky's bike and now he wants it back, but I can ride better'n him so why

92

always him . . ."

"It's *my* bike," one timid little boy, Nicky presumably, ventured, "I never even gave it to him . . ."

"You didn't, what?" I fumed, "Because he's a redhead!" I carried Amir home in my strong arms and washed the tears off his face.

"You are no redhead!" I said to him when he'd recovered from the washing, "You're not a redhead *at all!* Redheads have freckles on their nose, and you only have four, and even then only in summer. A true redhead is red in every way, not just in matters of hair! King David was a redhead, the best sort of animals are redheads, like foxes and . . . and . . . gingerbread! But you aren't, Amir, you're not a real redhead, not much . . ."

Think it made any difference? Not much! Once that boy gets an idea into his head, nothing will ever get it out again. He thinks redheads are special! I ask you! Is that the sort of thing they teach them at kindergarten? The other day I caught him in front of the mirror counting his freckles! That's what we've been afraid of all along, and now it's happened . . .

"Why?" said his mother sadly, "Why do they pick on them?"

Why indeed? My heart bleeds for the little gingers, especially for those whose parents don't know how to help them get rid of their complexes.

Me and It

One day I receive a note from Revenue, very official-looking indeed though the print is sort of wobbly. I open it and it says:

"Last warning before seizure. Having failed to discharge your debt to the amount of IL. 20,012.11 due for repairs carried out in Kishon Harbour between July 6–21, 1969, you are hereby notified that unless you pay above sum within seven days, we shall be obliged to enforce Regulation 238/a/5 re seizure of property and sale of same."

Thus spoke Revenue, ending on a note of mollification: "In case you have meanwhile discharged said debt, please disregard this notification." The whole was signed – B. Seligson, Chief, Exec., Dpt. of Rev.

I felt slightly puzzled. On the one hand, a careful check of my books and manuscripts revealed that no repairs whatever had been carried out upon me of late. On the other hand, I certainly couldn't claim to have discharged this debt they were speaking of. Still, I have always believed that local conflicts should be resolved through face-to-face negotiation, so I went to see Mr. Seligson of Revenue in person.

"Look," I said, pointing at my identity card, "I'm a writer, not a harbour."

The Chief Exec. gave me a piercing glance:

"Then how come you're called Kishon?"

"A question of habit," I explained, "But me, I'm Ephraim too, and the harbour isn't."

A good point. The Chief withdrew to talk it over with his

staff in the other room. I couldn't hear what they were saying, but now and then someone came and looked at me, and one even asked me to stand up and turn round. In the end they decided to accept my argument, or at least to give me the benefit of the doubt, and Seligson himself came back and cancelled the Last Warning. He wrote "owns no harbour — Seligson" in red on my file, and drew a nice round zero with a cross on the cover. I gave a sigh of relief and went home.

"It was all a mistake," I told my wife, "Cold logic won the day."

"See?" the little woman declared, "You're always such a pessimist."

The notice about "Seizure of Goods and Chattels" arrived on a Wednesday some ten days later. "Having failed to act on previous notification re dischargement of IL. 20,012.11 debt," Mr. Seligson wrote in his familiar wobbly print, "I shall be obliged to enforce Regulation 238/a/5 re seizure of goods and chattels and sale of same. In case you have meanwhile discharged said debt, please disregard this notification."

I hurried back to Rev.

"I know, I know," Mr. Seligson said soothingly, "It's the computer sends these notifications, not me. It always does this sort of thing, don't take any notice . . ."

It turned out that Rev. headquarters in Jerusalem had gone over to automation about six months ago, and since that day the computer had been doing what some ten-thousand gloomy clerks had done before. This meant not only an end to bureaucratic foot-dragging, but also relief for all those clerks, who could now just sit back comfortably and watch. The only trouble with this computer was that its ministering technicians didn't quite know what went on inside it yet, and as a result they sometimes fed it things that gave it indigestion — as had happened with my harbour repairs. Chief Seligson promised that this time he'd fix the matter once and for all, and just so I wouldn't worry he sent off a message to the Jerusalem terminal at once, telling it to postpone my debt right away, on his responsibility. I thanked him for this noble gesture and went home in high spirits.

On Sunday they came for the fridge. The Government, that is, appeared on my doorstep in the shape of three hefty porters, who showed me an order signed by B. Seligson, then proceeded to seize my very good and chattel fridge and drag it out to a waiting lorry heedless of my protests.

"Look at me!" I shouted at them, "Do I look like a harbour? Do I sound like a harbour? Have you ever heard a harbour swear, damn you?"

But they were only obeying orders, and a mere mortal is helpless against that. I found Chief Seligson staring at the wall of his office in despair. He had just received notice from Jerusalem, warning him to discharge his debt of IL. 20,012.11 for repairs on me — or else.

"I suppose," he said, eyeing me reproachfully, "that that's how the computer interpreted that phrase about 'my responsibility'. I should have known. I should have been more careful. You've sure managed to get me into trouble, sir!"

I told him not to take any notice, but that didn't cheer him up much.

"Once a computer gets its hands on you, you're lost," he said despondently, "The other day someone at the Execution Department got orders from the computer to execute one of his deputies . . . The Minister himself had to intervene to save the poor fellow. They had him on the scaffold already . . ."

I said how if we went to Jerusalem to beard the computer in its den? "Come now, Comp," we'd say to it, "Lay off, will you?"

"It won't listen," thus Seligson, "It's too busy. It's the busiest bloody computer I know. They use it for everything there — elections, weather forecasts, horoscopes, everything."

Still, he did what he could, Chief Seligson, bless him. He rang up Storage and told them to hold up the sale of my fridge till further notice.

The fridge was auctioned off that evening for IL.19, as I learnt from the "Notification re Debt Outstanding" which the computer sent me next morning with unbureaucratic celerity. My debt had shrunk to IL.19,993.11, the which I was told to discharge within seven days. In case I had meanwhile . . . disregard . . .

Seligson wasn't in when I called, because he'd been busy – talking to his lawyer, registering his fridge in his wife's name, and such. When he did come in he swore that if he'd ever get out of the computer's clutches he'd never interfere with it again, no matter what. I said yes, but what am I going to do?

"Dunno," said the Chief, "Maybe the computer will forget about you. It does sometimes. All you can do is hope . . ."

I told him I couldn't wait for miracles, I wanted to settle this *now*. "Very well," said Seligson, "If you insist." We agreed after some argument that I would discharge the debt for repair of my harbour in 12 monthly instalments. I signed an IOU, and we rushed it off to Jerusalem to try and save what could be saved of my goods and chattels. "That's the best I can do," said Chief Seligson, "I'm sure they'll learn how to handle that computer in a year or two, but meanwhile . . . well . . ."

"Never mind," I consoled him, "Rome wasn't built in a day."

The first cheque for IL.1,666.05 arrived two days later. Enclosed was Seligson's note in the computer's wobble, informing me that this was a first payment on the IL.19,993.11 which I had been credited with in Jerusalem on September 4, 1969. I told the little woman we were set up for life, so she asked why didn't they pay us interest as well, they should, shouldn't they?

"Maybe," I said, "but I'm not going to lift a finger to get it. I know when I've had enough."

The future belongs to automation. Meanwhile disregard this warning.

Veni, Vidi—Oh, No!

Some time ago I brought my son Rafi a football field from abroad. This is a splendid sort of toy, not too different from the thing Tel Aviv's long-haired youth play with at the beach-front cafés. There's this green board with a goal at either end and a number of rods that cross the board breadthwise, each with a number of red or green wooden doll players attached to it. You turn a rod and your dolls head the small wooden ball towards your opponent's goal to gladden the heart of young and old alike. It's a delightful game, specially devised to develop a noble competitive spirit in your child and educate him towards true sportsmanship, as it says on the box.

Rafi took to it at sight. I admit that in the beginning he was remarkably clumsy at playing it, but it soon turned out that he had no aptitude for mini-football whatsoever. The child draws nicely and multiplies fractions in his head without any trouble, but as far as his two hands are concerned he shows extreme leftist tendencies. It's not that he doesn't twirl the rods. He twirls them, but the ball always goes off in every direction except the goal. I'm not unduly worried — the child draws such wonderful pictures in his exercise books that the teacher doesn't believe I made them, and he's only seven after all and very lively for his age, so there.

The trouble is that our little Butterfingers has a strong sense of winmanship. Whenever he pits himself against his classmates and is dealt another crushing defeat, his face turns as red as his dolls and big tears splash right on top of Pele's head. The worst of it is, you see, that Rafi is passionately keen on the game, so much so that he's even christened his own team: the forwards are called Pele, the goalie Franko, and all the rest are Fuchs. In view of the defeatist mood that has come over Rafi lately, and with good reason, he now refuses to play with anyone except me. What annoys me even more is that while we are engaged in noble competition, he keeps sending me mute looks, as if imploring me to "Lose, Daddy, lose!" I consider that rather unfair. What the hell, I don't want to lose either! Let him damn well play better! At his age I already trapped fully-grown insects in matchboxes and took whole alarm clocks apart . . .

I tried logic to make him see it my way:

"I'm big," I reasoned, "and you're little, right?"

"Uhu."

"What would you think of a daddy who was licked by his own little boy? Think such a daddy was any good?"

"Unh-unh."

"Then why do you get so miserable when I lick you?"

"Because," said Rafi between sobs, "I want to win!"

Here his mother intervened:

"Do let him beat you once, for heaven's sake," she whispered in my ear, "just to give him back his self-respect. You never know what damage to his ego . . ."

I made a superhuman effort to save Rafi's ego. Every time one of his Pele's aimed a kick at my goal I pulled my goalie politely out of the way, just to give my poor misfit a chance to for heaven's sake score at least one point over me, dammit! But no! At multiplying fractions he's good, very good even, but I guess he'll never manage to kick anything except his heels. As a last resort, therefore, I decided to take do-it-yourself measures and give myself a goal. I spun my green centre-forward's rod and – whoom! – the ball hit my crossbar – bounded back – cold sweat broke out all over me – and the ball rolled slowly and inexorably into Rafi's goal. . .

There now, he was blubbering again! Not only that, but the

excitable child swept up the entire field, goals, players and all, and dashed it furiously to the ground! "You're not letting me win!" he yelled. "You're doing it on purpose! . . ."

I picked up the game tenderly and saw that three of my green dolls had lost their heads . . . "Now you've gone and broken your toy," I pointed out gloomily, "My team won't be able to even touch the ball without heads . . ."

"Never mind," thus my flesh-and-blood, "let's carry on anyhow . . ."

And sure enough, as soon as we resumed our match the pace picked up. I turn and turn my beheaded players and it's as if they simply weren't there at all. The ball passes from Fuchs to Pele, from Pele I to Pele II, and at last — I raised the other end of the table a bit to make it slant my way — at last — hallelujah! — the ball went home . . .

"Hoho!" shouted Rafi, delirious with triumph — "Goal! 0:1! Hoho! I licked you! Three cheers for Israel! Yippee! Hoho! . . ."

Next morning all the players of my team were decapitated. *I* did that. For the sake of my eldest son's ego and general happiness. Since then I only twiddle the rods, but my midgets haven't a chance, whereas Rafi just kicks and kicks with unobstructed abandon till he scores a goal or two by mistake. His chin is up again, his voice rings clear, and his bearing has grown slightly aggressive. Last week we played a whole series. We called it "The Psychological Cup Matches".

The Crack of Doom

This crack didn't wait till doomsday, but appeared right on the first day of winter when some pipe burst in the wall of my room and a brownish stain started spreading across it. I gave the pipe two days to mend its own crack, and when it didn't I turned to Stucks, our plumber.

Stucks lives at the other end of town and is hard to get anyway. On Saturday I nevertheless caught him at Israel v. Italy, and, being in a good mood on account of the 2:1 at half-time, he promised to come if I'd fetch him in my car before he set out for work in the morning. He sets out for work at six. I asked him why before, didn't the work at my place count as work? Stucks said no.

So I fetched him at 5.30. Stucks glanced at the spreading stain and said:

"How can I get at that pipe, mister? You got to get a builder to open up the wall first . . ."

And he went, pointing out that now he'd lost a whole working day. I was left with my stain and my need of a builder. I don't know any builders. I asked around among friends, neighbours, colleagues, and none of them did either. In the end someone whose cousin used to be a contractor mentioned one Gideon, who is a handyman and might do. Gideon lives in the suburbs.

I caught Gideon early next morning on his way into town, but it turned out he could only come after work, at nine in the evening. I fetched him at nine, and Gideon glanced at the wall and said:

"How can I open up this wall, with water squirting all over the place? You got to get me a plumber to turn off the main first . . ."

I felt myself change colour. That's exactly what I'd been afraid of all along. Deep inside I had known, but tried to suppress the knowledge that yes, they would have to be here *together*. Stucks couldn't get at it without Gideon, and Gideon would get wet without Stucks.

Like a couple of space twins they were, who must meet on a certain date, at a certain point in space.

And *I* would have to set up the meeting.

It's easy enough to write the words — paper will take anything. But the mere thought of arranging a Stucks-Gideon Summit was enough to give me nightmares. The original Gemini Meet must have been child's play by comparison. Those guys at least work according to the same time schedule, whereas my Stucks is only free mornings and my Gideon only evenings, and East is East and West is West and . . .

I visited the Stucks end of town twice and the Gideon suburb three times to try and coordinate the twins, but in vain. I suggested they compromise between 5.30 in the morning and 9 in the evening, and meet each other halfway at 1.15 at night by my wall — but they only shrugged their shoulders. Nix. Then I came up with the tentative solution of a teeny weeny sinlet: let them come on the Sabbath. Stucks agreed, but Gideon takes the kids out sabbaths, he never sees them all week. The brownish stain was sprouting tentacles unchecked, and one freezing day I burst into tears on Gideon's doorstep. He took pity on me and produced his pocket-diary to see what could be done.

"Well," he said finally, "I see here how next Independence Day falls on a Monday, so that makes Sunday sort of like a sandwich, so I guess I'll take Sunday off too. How's that . . ."

I kissed him and rushed over to Stucks, but he only sniffed at the sandwich and wouldn't bite. Sunday? Why shouldn't he work on a plain Sunday?

"Then what shall I do, Stucks? What shall I *do*?"

"Ask me another," said Stucks, picking his teeth, "I can only come mornings and that's . . . Wait, though! . . ."

Providence had intervened at last. It so happened that next Tuesday evening Stucks was planning to go and see his brother-in-law who lives at my end of town, so maybe he'd drop in on me before — say at 7.30. Life is sweet, life is beautiful! With a song in my heart I drove back to Gideon's.

"Got it!" I shouted, "Got a plumber for you next Tuesday night!"

"Sorry," said Gideon, "Tuesday night I've got 'Fiddler on the.Roof '."

Omegod!

"Please," I whispered, "Please, couldn't you go to the theatre some other time? . . ."

"Yeah," said Gideon, "I could, but you can't expect me to rush around changing tickets and all . . ."

I wouldn't dream of it! Of course *I* would go to change them — it was *my* wall Brownie was eating up, not his.

To be brief, it wasn't quite as easy as you might think, but in the end I did manage to get Gideon his two tickets for the night of December 26. Back to Gideon's with the good news. This time it was his wife who opened the door — and informed me that no, the 26th wouldn't do, that was just when Grandma was bringing the kids back home. They'd been spending the week with her, you see, and . . .

"Couldn't they come home a day earlier?"

"Yeah," said Mrs. Gideon, "If it's all right with their Grandma . . ."

Their Grandma lives in Eilat. A dear old lady, full of good-will and that, but she doesn't travel on the Sabbath. And December 25th was a Sabbath.

"I'm not all that religious myself," Grandma confessed, "But my late husband did use to go to synagogue."

And for that my house should rot to pieces? I tried pleading with Grandma. I said I was sure that if her husband were alive he wouldn't mind letting the kids go on a Saturday, particularly if someone came to fetch them all the way from

Tel Aviv in his car . . .

"No," said Grandma, "No, I really mustn't. I mean, what would our rabbi say? . . ."

The rabbi, thank God, was at home.

"Dear Rabbi," I said, "If Grandma lets the kids go on Saturday, then Gideon can go to the theatre on the 26th, and then he'll be free to meet Stucks at my wailing wall on Tuesday at 7.30. If that isn't a matter of life and death I don't know what is."

The rabbi was an enlightened man, so Grandma agreed, so the kids, the Fiddler, Tuesday. I went to see Stucks, drunk with success.

"Got it!" I shouted wildly, "Got you a builder on Tuesday!"

"Sorry," thus Stucks, "My brother-in-law said to come Wednesday instead of Tuesday . . ."

Stucks, would you believe it, had even tried to phone and let me know, but the line had been busy or what. It seemed the brother-in-law had forgotten how on Tuesday he had this P.T.A. meeting. The stain had reached the ceiling.

"Yeah," said the brother-in-law, "Sure, if you can get them to move the meeting to another day, then why not?" So helpful as everybody is, really. Eighteen parents agreed to Thursday at once, and only three made difficulties. The hardest was a Mrs. Mitwoch who had people coming Thursday night. Four of her prospective visitors agreed to switch over to Friday, but one said he had no car and the buses didn't run Friday night, and two ladies had babies but no babysitters. I hired a car for the carless man, bribed my sister to babysit for one of the ladies, and killed the other and buried her in the garden.

Now the P.T.A. meeting was due for Thursday instead of Tuesday, and the way was open for my Gemini Meet.

At 7.30 we, the wall and I, were ready and waiting. We waited for three hours and no one came. At 10.50 Stucks said goobye to his brother-in-law, and at 11 he dropped in on me. Where was Gideon? Gideon had forgotten.

Fortunately the stain had gone too, or rather the wall had

gone, leaving only stain. So then I sold the flat and bought a new one. Funny that this simple solution shouldn't have occurred to me before.

Cocoa-Nut

My redheaded son Amir is a poor eater. He's been a poor eater from the cradle. He just doesn't like to chew. Or swallow Experienced mothers told us we should starve him – just starve him till he came begging for food on his knees. So we starved him – till Amir got so thin that we begged him to eat on our knees. Then we took him to see a famous specialist, and the man just glanced at our skinny son and asked:

"What's the matter with him? Doesn't he eat?"

"No."

"I thought so."

The specialist informed us that there was nothing to be done, some children were poor eaters and that was that. We paid him for his advice, and since then we've more or less resigned ourselves to the fact and just cram as much food into the child as he'll hold: by the sweat of our brows shall he eat. Actually we don't have much patience for all the bribing and such that's involved. My wife's father, on the other hand, loves it: he tells Amir the craziest stories, and Amir sits openmouthed and forgets not to eat.

The Problem with a capital "C" is Cocoa. Cocoa, as every child knows, is made up of nothing but what's good for you – vitamins, minerals, spinach, everything. And so, come evening, Gramps and Amir retire to the nursery, and after about an hour Gramps reappears, tired but happy:

"He's drunk half . . ."

The turning point came one summer evening when Gramps emerged from the nursery almost speechless with joy:

"He's drunk it all!"

"Gee," I said, "How did you do it?"

"I told him we'd pull Daddy's leg," my cunning father-in-law revealed, "I said let's drink all our cocoa and then fill the empty cup with water and tell you that we hadn't drunk any at all, and you'd be awfully cross, and then we'd say we'd fooled you . . ."

I did find it all a bit primitive, frankly, but under the wife's pressure ("So long as he *has* drunk his cocoa . . .") I played along. Gramps came out of the bathroom toting this cup with its disgusting mess and announced: "Amir hasn't drunk his cocoa!"

"Grrr, am I cross," said I, "Grrr, am I wild. Then I'll drink his cocoa myself!"

Amir's eyes sparkled with glee as I tasted the nasty stuff and spit it out in an arc:

"Ugh! What's this?"

"Fooled you! Fooled you!"

Amir danced round me like a little savage and his laughter rang like a bell — but he'd drunk his cocoa, and that, as his mother says, is what matters.

Next day — ditto. Gramps goes to the bathroom, grrr, am I cross, grrr, am I wild, spit in an arc (the only part that's natural), fooled you, fooled you. And from then on we go through the entire rigmarole every evening, and by now we don't even need Gramps any more (the child grows older and learns, after all). Amir goes to the bathroom himself, grrr, am I cross, fooled you, the glee, the bell . . .

In time it began to worry me, rather.

"Listen, my dear," I said to the wife, "Do you think this child of ours is a ninny?"

What bothered me, I mean, was what the hell does this child think? Does he think that after the zillionth repeat I *still* don't know what he's up to every evening? That I'm soft in the head? The little woman pointed out that never mind what the child thinks, so long as he drinks his cocoa. I did try to get to the bottom of it once: instead of tasting the bilge before the ugh-what's this, I poured it straight into the sink.

"But Daddy! You didn't taste it!" — and Amir burst into tears.

I got hot under the collar. What does he take me for? A child?

"I don't *have* to taste it," I yelled, "I can *see* it's water!"

"Then why did you always taste it before, you liar?"

Aha, so Amir *knows* we're only going through the same stupid motions night after night. He knows. So why do we have to go through them all the same?

"Because it amuses him," says the wife, "And so long . . ."

Autumn came and went, and some time in November my little cocoa-nut introduced a slight change into our dialogue, so that my cue now went: "I didn't drink any. This isn't cocoa at all, it's pee . . ."

And late in December he began stirring the muck with his little finger before handing it to me for spitting. I hated it more with every repetition. I'd started to dread the minute when the little monster would show up with his glee and his bell. Why can other kids drink their cocoa without the dramatics and only me, I'm stuck with this half-wit . . . Roundabout New Year I did a shocking thing. Something gave, I suppose. That evening I took the bitter cup from my son and did not spit the bilge out in an arc but drank it all to the last drop. It nearly choked me, but I just had to do it. Amir watched my performance with narrowed eyes, and then the storm broke:

"Why did you do that?" he wailed, "Why?"

"What d'you mean — why?" thus I, with a sick sort of satisfaction, "You told me you hadn't drunk any, and that this wasn't cocoa and all, right? And I said okay, then I'll drink it myself, so I drank it — so what?"

Amir looked at me with loathing and cried all night. What it all came down to was that he'd known all along that I knew it was water and was only pretending. But if that's so, then who needs this sickly comedy every night? The little woman solved this one for me:

"The child," she said, "drinks his cocoa, and that's all that matters."

So the cocoa make-believe went on, night after blasted night, and I almost stopped caring. A man can't be blamed for the stupidity of his offspring, after all. It's like a natural disaster, nothing you can do about it. Some parents are blessed with smart children, and others are not so blessed, grrr.

The next thing that happened was Amir's fifth birthday. That evening, instead of our usual fun and games, Amir had a proper party, and when his friends had all gathered he took them to his room, and he took the poison cup with him too. Presently the little woman sent me along to keep an eye on things, but as I reached the nursery door, I heard my son's voice, as follows:

"So now I've got to go to the bathroom to fill it with water."

"Why?" says Nicky.

"'Cause that's how my daddy wants it."

"Why?"

"Dunno, Same thing every night."

So that means — it means he thinks it's me — *I* need these games! He goes through the rigmarole for my sake! This child isn't dumb, ladies and gentlemen, this child is queer!

Next day I drew him aside.

"Son," I said to him, "Daddy wants to stop all this nonsense with the cocoa. It was fun while it lasted, but it's not educational. Let's invent some new game, huh?"

This time he cried for *two* nights, and my wife, too, nearly lost her patience with me.

"If the child stops drinking his cocoa too," she warned me, "he'll just shrink to nothing."

So the show must go on. Sometimes my son calls out from the bathroom: "Ready? I'm coming with the water!" — and I go through my lines on cue: "Grrr, am I cross, grrr am I wild," and profound despair grips me. One time Amir was in bed with measles, so I went to the bathroom myself, filled

109

the cup with water and drained it.

"Fooled you!" – my son's eyes sparkled with glee – "Fooled you!"

The other day he thought up a new variation on the old theme: he comes out of the bathroom with the muck and declaims my text himself: "Grrr, am I cross, grrr . . ." My brain reels.

"What the hell," I asked the woman, "Doesn't he know *he* is talking – not I? Or does he think it's *me* talking when *he* does? What's going on in this house?"

"Yeah" said the little one, "but."

The Calory Count-Down

"Ephraim," the little woman asked, "Do you think I'm fat?"

"No," said I, "No you're not."

"But you are!"

"Then so are you, Fatty!"

Actually we're neither of us fat in the full sense of the word. The woman may be a bit roly-polyish at the edges, and I somewhat prominent in profile, but that's a matter of how you look at it rather than what the scales say.

So then we went and joined the Weight Watchers anyway, because we like to be *in*. Also, the little one's friends kept telling her all these monster-to-midget stories, like how this girl lost 90 pounds in a month, which may not sound like much to you but was a fortune for the poor girl.

At the Weight Watchers we were received by one lady who needed watching herself, and one lean gentleman who served as Good Example.

"Only three months ago he used to offer his seat in the bus to *two* old ladies," we were told, "Now he's a ballet dancer."

Here the ballet dancer took over to explain the W.W. rules. As soon as you join, he said, we open a file against you. Then you pay your membership dues, and for that you receive a weekly brainwashing and a printed menu. Now, don't worry, you don't have to stop eating, only give up the good things in life. Bread, butter, spaghetti, schnitzel are out. So are peas, beans, nuts, and above all starches. No starches! Kohlrabi, on the other hand, you may eat as much as you like. Cabbage too. Some milk, and plenty of fish. Exercise is no good because it only makes you hungry. The best thing to do is to lie flat on the floor and take a glass of tepid water once a week. At the end of it you come here to be weighed, and if you aren't found wanting you should be ashamed of yourself. If you are, you get a pat on the back and are sent home for more of the same.

"Splendid," I said, "I never did like exercise."

Next the lady took us away to be weighed — shoeless but with our keys.

"Sorry," she said, "You aren't overweight enough."

Our spirits sank. That such a petty formality should keep us from joining the Great Family of Watchers! The maddening part of it was that I myself was only six lbs. short of the required minimum, and the little one, being little, only three. They said we were lucky to be disqualified together, sometimes they had to send only one half of a couple home. People get divorced for less.

We, at any rate, went home together and started eating our way through the entire list of forbidden foods, till we felt we'd qualify at least as border cases. Then we trudged back to the W.W., and just to be on the safe side I filled my pockets with IL.50 in small change — and tipped the scales!

"Welcome to the W.W." said the lady, "Now I can open a file for you."

The Good Example gave us our orders: "Three big meals a day," he said, "Don't starve yourselves. And vary, vary! If you get sick of cabbage, by all means switch to cauliflower. And remember: starch is poison! See you next week . . ."

We returned home and started on our diet. Our cheese was invariably white and lean, our bread green and cucumber. Then we went back to be weighed, and died with shame because we had gained three ounces without a penny in our pockets.

"Yes," the lady pointed out, "I've seen it happen before. You'll have to be stricter with yourselves."

So then we ate nothing but kohlrabi for a week, and we didn't gain weight but we didn't lose any either. We felt badly let down, and were sent to talk it over with some fellow W.W.'s to boost our morale. It turned out that the same thing had happened to them: it's a case of one's body refusing to cooperate. It just won't count calories, and what can you do?

"Skip a meal a day," one veteran Watcher suggested.

"Go swimming," said another, "And show your body what it feels like to weigh less."

The little one had meanwhile discovered an old pharmacy where the scales were out of order, but half the women of Tel Aviv were always queuing up in front of it, and anyhow, cheat as you may — truth will out at the W.W. We soon realized we were stuck: no gain, no loss. I looked at the little one and, frankly, I was surprised: how come she wasn't losing weight? I did have a vague idea why I wasn't — I was moonlighting in the kitchen every night . . . The kohlrabi was getting its own back.

Actually I guess it was simply the seven-week itch: I woke up one night with an irresistible urge to smell the sweet smell of hot oil, and I knew I just had to fry something or I'd bust. I wanted starch, lovely starch . . .

I jumped out of bed, tiptoed to the kitchen and emptied an enormous bag of popcorn into a pot of boiling oil. I sprinkled sugar over the white mountain by the spoonful and devoured the lot — fat, starch, poison and all. That was the beginning of my calory binge. It was potato crips one night and whipped cream the next, and I really had a lovely time, even if rather tiring on account of the double life I was leading now — days of legal, limitless kohlrabi, and nights of cake and ale . . .

Ephraim, I would warn myself, you'd better start smoking before it's too late.

And then the confrontation came.

One midnight I'm standing by the stove frying bananas when the sleepy figure of my wife enters, makes straight for the laundry basket and digs up a dozen bars of milk chocolate.

She peels off the first wrapper, and with her mouth full throws me a conspiratorial wink and generously offers me a bar . . .

We sat there for half an hour eating chocolate, till all of a sudden my instinct for self-preservation woke, I crawled to the telephone and dialled the W.W. with the last of my strength.

"Come quick . . . we're eating . . . chocolate . . ."

"Hold on!" the Example on duty yelled back, "We're coming!"

The car pulled up with a squeal of brakes. They kicked down the door and found us out cold under the table amid the torn wrappers. They only managed to save the last two bars.

"Never mind, dears," the Good Example comforted us, "This happens to everybody: you regain in an hour what you've lost in a year of kohlrabi. Then you start from scratch . . ."

"Please," we begged, "No more kohlrabi."

"All right. Lettuce."

But we decided to leave the W.W. instead. We were failures, and we knew it.

So now I am prominent in profile again, and the little one roundish at the edges, but so what? Fat people are kind, they're cheerful, and they rarely fly off the handle, on account of the time it takes for the anger to spread through them. They aren't aggressive either because they can't run.

A Bit of Cabala

Man is an enigma. Jewish man is a mystery. A Jewish man who's a pedlar too is something past comprehension.

This pedlar first turned up on our doorstep some three years back. He climbed the stairs, rang every doorbell on the way, and if someone opened he'd raise his little suitcase a bit and ask:

"Soap? Razor blades?"

And people would say:

"Thanks, nothing we need."

"Toothbrush – flexible?"

"No, thanks."

"Hairpins?"

"No!"

"Toilet paper?"

At which point we shut the door in his face. Thereafter the pedlar came twice a month, rang, said his piece, we'd shut the door, and that was that. Once in a mellow mood I offered him a few pennies but the man protested. "I'm no beggar, sir!" he said, and gave me a reproachful look. The other day was his day again. He rang. I opened.

"Soap?" he went, "Razor blades?"

A sudden fit of generosity took me:

"All right," I said, "Give me a razor blade."

"Toothbrush?" the pedlar went on, "Flexible?"

"Yes. A razor blade."

"Hairpins?"

"Are you deaf or something?" I flared up, "I said I wanted

115

a razor blade."

"A what?"

"A razor blade!"

He looked at me, absolutely flabbergasted.

"Why?"

"A razor blade," I hissed, "I — want — to buy — a razor blade!"

"Toilet," the pedlar whispered, "paper . . ."

"For Pete's sake!" I cried impatiently, took the suitcase from his hand and opened it. The suitcase was empty. There was nothing in it.

"What's this mean?"

The pedlar lost his temper:

"Nobody ever buys nothing from me!" he shouted angrily, "So what should I *shlep* all this stuff for?"

"Quite," I agreed soothingly, "But . . . but in that case . . . why go from door to door?"

"A man's got to make a living somehow, no?"

And with that he took his leave, crossed the landing and rang the Seligs' doorbell.

Born Free

Things keep happening in our household, I don't know why. There was, for instance, the day the little woman came and told me we needed a new washing machine. I asked why, and she said the old one was getting old. I said all right, so go buy yourself a young one, but no more than one, mind you, and no fancy foreign brands, we've got to encourage the local industry.

She's a great one for buying, is the little one, and the very next day a handsome young Sabra washing machine with plenty of knobs on was already humming away merrily on our back-porch. It was a case of love at first wash: this machine could do everything on its own, from feeding itself soap-flakes to spinning itself dry, as if endowed with a human brain.

And that's just it.

On that Tuesday about noon my wife came to me with a slightly puzzled frown on her face, and said:

"Ephraim, it walks!"

I followed her to the kitchen porch and sure enough, our new washing machine, while busily spin-drying, was at the same time moving with great leaps towards the kitchen. We brought it to a standstill right on the doorstep by pressing the red button, and took account of the situation. Before long we discovered that it only walked as it spin-dried, seeing that this drum thing inside made it shake all over and then — hop! hop! hop! — it started jumping about as if moved by some irresistible urge.

We didn't mind, really. Our house is no prison, after all, and if this machine felt like taking a stroll round the backyard, we saw no reason to stop it.

It turned out, that we had been rather too permissive.

One evening we suddenly hear a loud metallic crunch out there on the back-porch, and when we go to investigate we find Amir's tricycle lying all twisted underneath our spin-drying machine. The child cried like a child and beat his little fists against the sides of the offending gadget:

"Look what you've done, you naughty Wachine, look what you've done! . . ."

We tried to explain to him that the Wachine hadn't done it on purpose, that it had just been roaming about a little, found this tricycle and — hop! — jumped up on it, but Amir wouldn't listen to reason.

"There's nothing for it," said the wife, "I'll have to tie Jonathan up . . ."

And she took a piece of string and tied our washing machine to the hot-water tap. I didn't feel too happy about it, but said nothing: it was her machine, after all, and she could tie it up if she wanted to. Still, I can't deny that when we discovered Jonathan at the other end of the porch next morning, I was tickled pink. He had strained all the horse-powers he had and broken his bonds. The woman only frowned and went for a new piece of string. This time she tethered him to the gas tanks, with the result that when he broke loose we not only heard it, we smelt it.

In the end the woman gave up since, as she said, it only made Jonathan nervous to be put on the leash. From then on we let him do his washing untrammelled. Our machine, we told ourselves, was a noble Israeli creature — a free, independent Sabra spirit. It only caused trouble once, when we were having some people over and it burst into the living room suddenly and frightened our guests . . .

"Get out!" cried the wife, "Out! Go back where you belong!"

As if a washing machine can understand what you're

saying to him! Huh. I calmly got up and pressed the red button, and that was that. Later, after our visitors had left, I restarted Jonathan in order to lead him back, but, like the lilies of the field, he toiled not, neither did he spin. What had happened was that he'd already passed the spin-drying stage and, as you may remember, he only walked when he spun. We had to go through the whole process again to make him budge . . .

Amir, in the meantime, had made his peace with Jonathan too, and loved to get up on his back and sit there shouting, "Giddy-up, giddy-up!"

Charming. Jonathan does our laundry beautifully too, goes easy on the soap-flakes, and except for this tendency of his to wander off now and then is altogether delightful.

Actually the little woman even suggested we make use of Jonathan's mobility — like send him to the grocery, she said, why not? I thought it wouldn't work, though. We'd have to give him a shopping list because he can't talk, and then he might lose the list or, worse, get lost himself and never find his way home again. No point taking the risk just to save my wife a trip to the grocery. On the other hand, Jonathan does love going out into the street. The little woman told me that Nicky's parents who live across the street have got a new washing machine, a very pretty, *petite* Italian. Could that be it? Could Jonathan . . .? The last thing we want is a houseful of little washing machines. Eventually I went to see a specialist who, it appeared, was quite familiar with our problem.

"Yes," he said, "I know the sort. They run when they spin. But they only do it if you put too little laundry in the drum: it upsets the centrifugal balance and jolts the machine. You ought to put a full load of at least eight lbs. in, and then I promise you your Jonathan will be quiet as a lamb . . ."

At home I found the little one weeding the garden, and informed her that our Jonathan only went on a centrifugal rampage for lack of dirty linen in his belly. The wife went pale:

"Good gracious!" she exclaimed, "And just today I only put four lbs. in . . ."

Together we raced to the porch. Our worst fears had come true: Jonathan was gone. *With* his electric cord. I rushed out.

"Jonathan!" I called, "Jonathan!"

I ran up and down the street, asking people if they'd seen a Hebrew washing machine anywhere, but nobody had. After an hour's search I gave it up and went home, feeling terrible. Maybe he'd got himself run over by a bus. Our Jonathan, free son of the industrial jungle, facing the dangers of the big city and its merciless bus drivers. Or maybe he'd come to the end of his spin in the middle of the road and could no longer move . . . Maybe he was standing there paralysed in a whirl of traffic right now . . .

"Found him!" — the woman came running to meet me — "He's here!"

It turned out that while the wife was in the garden, the silly little thing had wandered off into the passage, had reached the basement steps, and had been stopped at the last moment by pulling his plug out of the socket — thus saving himself from a certain death.

"Enough!" the little woman said grimly, "Get out of your clothes!"

She went and collected every article of clothing in the house and stuffed Jonathan with a full nine lbs. of washing. Jonathan toiled and spun — and stayed rooted to the spot like a lily. For weeks after, the woman would overload him like that and he just worked and worked. My heart bled for him.

One day I could stand it no longer.

I stopped him in mid-spin and removed some three lbs. of clothing from his drum. Jonathan took a few joyous leaps, then made straight for the pretty Italian across the street. He was humming loudly — the picture of a happy washing machine.

"Go, Jonathan!" — I patted his trembling flanks — "Go!" And he went.

A Hanging Matter

Personally I always used to have a healthy respect for heaven, but that winter I positively learnt to fear it.

It was on a Monday in December that we woke up in the morning, glanced through the window and said — Yippee! The heavens were as clear as an angel's conscience, and as blue as blue. The girls in the family — my little wife, that is, and her mother — jumped briskly out of bed and said — At last! We'd been waiting ages for a day like this, in order to get through the incredible quantities of dirty washing that had collected in a whole month of rain-rain-rain. The laundry basket had filled to overflowing, and we had been reduced to hiding our soiled linen in such out-of-the-way spots as under the bed and inside my desk drawers.

And now, finally, sunshine, you are my sunshine. Jonathan, it's true, happened to be on sick-leave just then, but wife and ma-in-law attacked the laundry with great enthusiasm themselves, and had washed their way through the lot in a mere five hours. Then we carried the whole caboodle by pailfuls to the garden and strung it up on the clotheslines, the antennae, the balcony railing, the fence, and the steel cable supporting the pole in front of our house for the benefit of the Electric Corporation. It was a hell of a job, and it took us the best part of an hour, but finally the last sock was up, hallelujah.

And then it started to rain.

Don't ask me how. Only minutes before, the sky had been smiling at us, you had to get up on the roof to see a cloud — and now all of a sudden it was raining. Did I say raining? The

121

sky had gone pitch-black, and big fat clouds were gathering from all over the world to hold a meeting over our garden. We raced about plucking everything off the clothesline, antennae, etc. again, ran to the bathroom and dumped it in the tub — and for the last batch we had to use a ladder because the laundry-mountain had reached the ceiling and beyond. Then we sank panting into an armchair, picked up the paper and looked at the weather forecast: partly cloudy in the morning, clearing up towards noon, it said, so we knew the storm would last a fortnight. It did. Outside it came down in torrents, and inside the wash fermented in our bathtub like beer in a barrel. By next morning our house smelt like a cellar with a dead body in it, and a lot of tiny green fungi had appeared on our walls.

"We've got to do something," the little woman announced, "Dry the stuff somehow before it rots in the tub."

We looked out: the cloud congress was still in full swing up there. No use waiting any longer. We took the longest piece of string we could find, and began putting it up in the living room. The string issued forth from the window-latch, ran through the cupboard key, from there to the doorknob, next to the button on the mirror-frame, then up-up-up to the lampshade and down again to the table leg, where it took a U-turn and came safely back home to the window-latch. The effect was rather stunning, not at all unlike some of the best of conceptual art.

We removed the laundry from the tub — I swear it was wetter than ever — and hung it up on our modern art line. Then we lit our dumpy kerosene stove to hurry up the drying process, and sat back with the satisfaction of knowing a good job well done. Life in our household resumed its normal course, except that every time we crawled through the living room we got soaking wet, both on account of the puddles on the floor and the water dripping on our back from the crisscross laundry line. Ma-in-law said a bat could fly between lines like that without even touching them, seeing it's got this radar or what, but that's cold comfort to me. Whatever else I

122

am, a bat I'm not.

The next thing that happened was that we sat down to dinner, and we'd just finished the soup when we heard something go — pingggg! whooshhh! — and the whole house shook and settled gently on its side. We raced for the living room and were met by a scene of utter havoc. Our string had decided that this burden was too much for it after all, and had snapped at the mirror-button station. Its load had thereupon crashed to the floor, where it now sprawled helpless like a Gulliver among the Lilliputians. I need hardly add, perhaps, that our best damask tablecloth, the pride of the family, had landed on top of the stove, with fearful consequences to both the stove and it.

For a moment we just stood there and stared. Then, without a word, we each grabbed an armful of the damp smelly stuff, rushed out into the pouring rain with it, and hung it all up again on the antennae, the railing, the fence, and the Electric Corporation cable. It's been there ever since, flip-flopping in the wind and the rain, getting wetter and dirtier by the day, but who cares — in here it's warm and dry, and we can walk upright in our own living room again. One day the sun will come out and dry our laundry, and then we'll take it down and burn it.

The Longest Night

Every miracle lasts a week, as our Sages have pointed out, and they're right. Take television. The first week or so we were positively mad about the box and stayed glued to it for nights on end. Today? We're still glued to it for nights on end — but mad? Na, not us! The only trouble is that our house stands on top of a hill, which makes for perfect reception, and we can catch the programmes of all our neighbours round, friends and foes alike, as far as Cyprus. The real victim of this technical accident is Amir, who has become utterly enslaved to the set. It's sick, really: he's capable of sitting in front of the screen for a full hour, his eyes fixed in a blank stare on the words, "Jordan Television, Channel Six". If you ask him what he's doing for chrissake he only says: "Shhh!"

Now of course one can think of better things for a child of five to do than watch television all day till midnight, the more as he has to get up and go to kindergarten in the morning. The situation deteriorated even further when Cyprus started their educational series, "The Gun Toters", teaching our son in nightly instalments how to kill a man without really trying. Now he has to have the light full on in his bedroom, he's scared of getting into bed, and once he's in he can't sleep but just lies there waiting for the killers to come and get him.

One day, therefore, the little woman decided to put an end to it.

"Enough," she said firmly, "It's eight o'clock — Amir is

124

going to bed!"

It turned out that, rather than a statement of fact, this was but the expression of a motherly wish: Amir isn't the chap to take such an order lying down.

"No!" he shrieked, "I want to see television! Te-le-vi-sion!!!!"

"You'll be dead tired in the morning," said his mother, "Do go to sleep, darling, it's way past your bedtime."

"Then why isn't it past *your* bedtime?"

"We're grownups."

"So you got to work in the morning, no?"

He's a tough bargainer. If needs be he can throw in a few juicy terms in Russian too.

"Why just me?" he went on, "Why always me? Why not you too?"

"Maybe you've got something there," said I with the diplomatic instinct of a born father, "Know what? We'll go to bed too!"

We killed the picture, yawned hugely, and climbed into our pyjamas *en masse*. Except what? Except they had "I Love Bessie" on Cairo that night, and I love Bessie too. We therefore kissed Amir goodnight tenderly and tiptoed right back into the living room. Softly we flicked the switch, and in no time the screen came to life and showed us the familiar figure of our son Amir standing before it livid with rage:

"So that's it!" he shouted, "*Me* they send to bed, and *they* stay up and have fun! Traitors!"

"Don't call your daddy traitors," his mother rebuked him. "We were just checking something, and now we'll all go to bed. *Good night!*"

So then we all stretched ourselves and went to bed and to sleep.

"Ephraim," whispered my wife in her sleep, "He should be off by now. Let's . . ."

"Shhh! Here he comes!"

He was standing in the doorway, squinting at us through the dark. I started snoring loudly, and the little woman breathed in and out quite audibly too. Amir watched for a while, then went back to his own bed to be scared of boogies. We gave it another few minutes in case he should return for a double-check, but as all remained quiet we sneaked warily back to the living room.

"Careful now!" said the woman, "Turn the sound off!"

Good idea. The picture's the thing, after all, and with a bit of practice at lip-reading you can get the drift of what's being said as well. But for that you need a good sharp image on the screen, right? The woman went and turned the contrast-dial as far as it would go, except that she missed in the dark and turned up the volume instead. The sound came on like the roar of a wounded lion . . .

Amir, however, can outroar a lion any day.

"You b . . .!" he went, "You b . . .! You cheated me! You cheated me! CHEATS!"

He stayed with us all through Bessie by way of punishment and then, still sobbing, watched Kojak crack a dope-ring on Channel Six. Next morning he dragged himself off to his kindergarten with bags under his eyes and fell asleep in the middle of Little Red Riding Hood, a story he's heard before.

"Very well," the little woman told him crossly, "We're going to sell this TV set, and that's it!"

"Fine, so sell it!"

But we didn't. We're not going to have our children dictate to us, we're still the boss in this household. That night we switched off at 8.15 and went up to brush our teeth. Then Amir watched us get into bed and retired to his own room. I dropped off at once, secure in the knowledge that I'd set the alarm clock at 9.30, as we wanted to pass the double-check convincingly asleep. It worked too. The muffled ring of the clock under my pillow woke us in time, but then an unforeseen obstacle came up:

"Good gracious!" said the woman, "He's locked us in!" So he had, with a chair on the outside for added safety. He's a bright child, is Amir. Too bad he's nuts.

"Wait!" I told the woman, "I know what!"

I climbed up on the window-sill, jumped down into the garden, went round to the living-room balcony, forced the door, went upstairs, moved the safety-chair and released the woman. All this took time, and we missed the opening chorus of "Oklahoma" on Beirut, but caught the tail-end of "Oh what a wonderful mo-o-orning," albeit in dumbshow as we'd turned off the sound, of course. Amir's part of the house was silent as well. Too silent? Whatsisname was mutely wooing the farmer's daughter now. The tension became unbearable . . .

"Listen!" I said to the woman, "What's that?"

"Oh God!"

The little one made a dash for the set, turned it off, and we both dived behind the couch. Amir, armed with a stick, could be heard making his way to the door of our bedroom. There he inspected the chair, tapped it with his stick, and sniffed all round it like a little bloodhound. "We're selling," I swore to myself, "We're selling the bloody box tomorrow."

"Hey!" Amir called sharply, "You asleep in there?"

He repeated the question a few times, and when he received no answer he opened the door.

The game was up. I turned on the living-room lights.

"Yoo-hoo, Amir," I called laughingly, "Fooled you, ha-ha!" Why go into details? I didn't mind the swearing so much, though I expect our neighbours must have been pretty shocked. The upshot was that Amir took his bedclothes and moved into the living room for good. He didn't trust us any more, apparently. Since then he's been living down there by the set, and sometimes he falls asleep in front of it towards dawn. I know. I counter-checked. What of it, though? Other people's kids smoke pot and tie cans to cats' tails, ours only watches television. Anyhow, we're going to sell the wretched thing tomorrow. Or else in a couple of days or some time. Sell it, and buy a new one.

Josepha the Free

The following story will, I'm afraid, be appreciated only by professional parents, students, and babies. It is the story of an Israeli babysitter or, to be precise, of our last sitter but one.

When we moved out of noisy Tel Aviv into the green suburbs, we gave up the services of our faithful Regina and went over to academic babysitting. Once in a while, that is, we pick a pretty student from the nearby campus, philosophy or comparative literature by preference, and give her the run of our brood. The kids soon grow fond of her and everything's fine, till one day the machine starts to creak and all of a sudden our cutie isn't free in the evenings any more, and she's got exams, and she can only come Wednesday, and even then she does her cramming with Gideon, and we come home Wednesday night and they're both on the couch with pink ears from much hard studying, and the cushions are crumpled and Gideon is combing his hair, and the wife says to me:

"That little hussy's already found herself someone."

And there, as a rule, the career of one babysitter ends and the next one enters the picture.

This time it was Josepha.

She already looked promising on sight: so small she was, so fragile, so bespectacled. The little woman took her for a girl of 13, but it turned out she'd already passed the 20 on her thin little legs. Josepha invariably wore slacks, and instead of speaking she rustled — a few words at a time, and with lowered eyes. Numerous moles dotted her little white face, and in fact, that's just what she looked like herself: a little mole. All in all, she seemed like an ideal, long-play babysitter.

Sure enough, Josepha came up to expectation. She'd show up on the dot, rustle "hi", and settle down in the kids' room to copy out something into one of her numerous notebooks. She never read, did Josepha, she never wrote, she just copied all the time, and that got us rather but we said nothing. Nobody is perfect, after all, except Amy. Still, Josepha came a close second, because unlike all our other academic baby-sitters, she was always free. Always. Never mind *when* we'd summon her, she'd always whisper back into the phone at once: "Yes, I'm free."

"Could you come a bit earlier?"

"Yes."

"And stay late?"

"Yes."

And before long she'd come to copy, softly and with downcast eyes.

I'd drive her home at night, and you could hear a pin drop in the car. I did crack under the strain once, to ask her what they were teaching in Comp. Lit. these days, and Josepha rustled: "Thank you," and that put an end to our lively conversation.

In every other way, however, she was the model sitter: ever soundproof, ever free, ever Josepha. We were very happy with her, and the kids, too, respected her Trappist silence, thin as she was. Once or twice we tried inviting her to join us for supper, but she only shook her head and looked scared. My wife was of the opinion that she never ate. Josepha, according to the wife, was a bit queer altogether.

"The poor thing," she said, "I mean, it just isn't natural that a young girl like that should always be free, is it?" It *was* pretty funny, come to think of it. Mornings, evenings, a quarter past three in the afternoon — Josepha was always ready to come and copy-sit. We rang her up at 11.45 p.m. once, when even the frogs were asleep already:

"Are you free?"

"Yes."

"Could you come right away?"

"Yes."

The wife hung up with tears in her eyes. "It's a regular tragedy," she said, "The girl hasn't got anyone, not anyone in the whole wide world . . ."

This period of compassion and maternal worry lasted a month. Then I found my wife getting a bit mad at Josepha. "You'll admit it's peculiar," she grumbled, "She's got an emotional block or something, that girl . . ."

The thing actually began to bother my wife. Once, after the usual phone-call, she went and pounded the wall with her fist:

"She's free again! FREE!"

Then came the Saturday when the little woman slipped out of bed at 2.30 a.m. and sleepwalked to the phone:

"Josepha, are you free?"

"Yes."

"Now?"

"Yes."

"Oh . . . well . . . never mind . . ."

By then she'd already taken a deep dislike to the girl. She had concluded that Josepha must be unbalanced. Something hereditary, perhaps, or something from way back in her childhood. A vision of Josepha at 12 appeared before our eyes — sitting in class and looking no doubt like a girl of seven.

"These are my favourite pupils," says the teacher, "Tirza the smart one, Ziva the cheerful, and Josepha the free."

And on Independence Day she was free too. Yes, on Independence Day, can you beat it? All that night she babysat and copied. The little woman was desperate:

"That a girl her age shouldn't have *one* lousy boyfriend," she wailed, "Why the hell doesn't she ever get out of those pants then? And do something about those ghastly moles? Who does she think she is anyway?"

My wife also said she was sure there was nothing wrong with Josepha's eyes, and she only wore glasses to put off all comers. At this point I thought I'd better do something or the wife would go crazy herself. I consulted our doctor and he suggested I find some excuse to ask the grown sons of our neighbours to drop in on Josepha's evenings. I did, with the result that Josepha just sat at her table and copied, absolutely petrified. She'd offer the boys a damp, trembling hand like a bird's broken wing, and rustle at the floor: "Josepha, howdo . . ."

The wife just went to pieces: "Josepha my foot," she snorted, "That's a Joseph if ever I saw one!"

The turning point came in the shape of Naftali, little-Ronit-on-our-left's big brother. This stalwart young man wasn't put off by our frozen babysitter like all the other candidates, but sat down by her side and followed the copying with profound interest, speechless as yet, but still. In the end they shook hands, as the wife informed me later, and passions began to stir.

"Maybe," whispered the woman, "Maybe this time . . ."

And that Tuesday it happened. The wife rang Josepha to ask if she'd be free that night, and the line hummed with the sensational reply:

"No."

"What do you mean no?" said the woman.

"I mean I can't . . ."

It was a time of rejoicing for us all — the triumph of sheer will power over social deprivation.

We stayed home happily that night, basking in a sense of achievement. Josepha had found someone at last, Josepha was free no longer, thank God. What's more, the effect of that handshake was lasting, and from then on the pace accelerated.

"Sorry," Josepha would rustle over the phone, "I'm busy."

"Busy," she'd said, like a big girl. Delicious.

"And tomorrow?"

"Only till nine . . ."

Good! We were as proud of her as parents of their baby's first tooth. We'd got the poor kid back in step after all, we'd saved a Jewish maiden from eternal spinsterhood. So we stayed at home well content, and the only thing that bothered us a little was that we were staying at home, and couldn't go out on account of Josepha. It was really disgusting. You'd have expected more loyalty from a girl you'd picked out of the gutter with your own two hands.

When we heard that Josepha and Naftali had been seen walking in the park by moonlight, while we ourselves were confined to barracks, the woman's dam burst:

"The little hussy!" she said, "The first boy that whistles – she runs . . ."

We'd have switched the little sex maniac for another copyist without thinking twice, except that the kids stuck out for Josepha, no doubt fascinated by something about her: legs, specs, dunno. So whenever we got her "Sorry, I can't tonight" on the phone again, we just swallowed the insult. What could we do?

Our cup of bitterness overflowed on the dark night of July 21, when we'd got Grandma to babysit and gone to the movies. Coming home we spotted a young couple standing under a lamp-post in deep and meaningful silence – *them!*

"G'night," rustled Josepha as we passed, whereupon the little one could no longer contain herself:

"My dear," she spat at the little hussy, "I thought you were working for an exam!"

"She is," said Naftali gallantly, "She studies all the time. Only tonight she's been babysitting for us and I'm just taking her home . . ."

Josepha cast her eyes down lower than ever, and took herself and her bogus moles off into the night. The woman swore softly, and I took a silent vow then and there, under that lamp-post, that from now on I'd pick nothing but cuties, nothing but smashing blond cuties to babysit for us, biology or physics.

There's a Hole in the Bucket

Remember Noah? Well, he had an ark, but we only have a house in the suburbs, and when the windows of heaven opened upon us, the fountains of the deep broke up too. At noon, that is, when I came home, I was met by my jubilant kids who reported:

"Daddy! The wall in our cellar is doing pee-pee!"

"Rubbish," I said, and would have stuck by that judgement too, if it hadn't been that our cellar was rapidly turning into a swimming pool. The wall wasn't peeing, it was squirting water like a geyser. Moses would have loved it.

We were a bit worried, to be sure, but we didn't lose our heads:

"We're being flooded!" shrieked the little woman, and ran out into the storm wringing her hands, "Flooded! Help! In the cellar! Water! Police! Army! Somebody help! Water!..."

As for me, I calmly leaped for the phone and called up our plumber, the Great Stucks himself. Stucks saw no reason for panic:

"It can't be the plumbing," he assured me, "I guess it's only water, you know, like a flood."

"But what do I do, Stucks, what do I *do*?"

"It'll be summer soon."

"Yes, but for now?"

"For now you'd better start bailing, or you'll have the whole house collapse on you."

The wife had meanwhile come in, and was trying to seal up the crack in the wall — first with bubblegum, then with the kids' plasticine, and lastly with a band-aid, which shows you the way water affects some people. On the brink of despair she suddenly remembered the little Dutch boy and stuck her finger in the hole — and that did it. Not all by itself, naturally, but in combination with someone else, meaning me, filling two buckets, dashing up the stairs and emptying them in the garden, then running back to our torture cellar again, fill the buckets, dash, empty, run, and keep that finger in the hole, for God's sake . . .

Still, I'm no Aquarius, and after half an hour of running around with two buckets I was about ready to drop. On top of that, I was getting more and more exasperated by the sight of Amir happily sailing paper boats in the cellar and enjoying himself no end. I said nothing, however, and was rewarded by the Municipality sending their motor pump along at last. They pumped out the water to the last drop and left, and within minutes the cellar had filled up again and I'd gone back to my dash-empty-run act, while the woman stuck her finger back in the dyke . . .

Then the phone went. Felix Selig. *Now* he wants to come and visit.

"Felix," I said hoarsely, "Felix, do me a favour . . ."

But here the little one came flying up the stairs and tore the receiver out of my hand:

"But of course, Felix," she said, "We were just going to have tea. Do come and join us. . ."

* * *

Not that the little one is smarter than me or anything. She just happened to have more presence of mind right then, as *she* only had to plug up the hole with her finger, while *I* was killing myself trying to bail out our Augean cellar like a modern Sisyphus. Not Sisyphus. Hercules. Somebody. Presently the Seligs arrived, and the little one went up to meet them.

"You'll never believe what just happened," she said, "A few minutes ago something gave in the cellar, and it's all under water. I don't know *what* I'll do . . . Poor Ephraim is down there fighting the flood singlehanded. It's awful . . . He'll drown (sob, sob) . . . I'm sorry, but you'd better go home. We'll manage somehow . . ."

"My dear!" said Felix indignantly, "I wouldn't think of leaving you . . ."

And with that he threw off his coat like a man, rolled up his trouser legs and joined me on the bucket run, while his wife and the little woman took turns with the finger-work. That, dear reader, is what I call true friendship, that's what I call solidarity. Felix, it turned out, *was* a water-carrier: before an hour was out the water had stopped rising in the cellar, and soon it only stood ankle high. We were grateful beyond words.

"You darlings," breathed the wife, sprawling in a chair, "We'd have been absolutely lost without you. Listen, though – I think there's no point hauling up only half a bucket at a time. Better fill it up to the brim . . ."

By now Felix was looking rather grim, and the water line had crept up again too, but we were lucky, because just then Zvika came round to ask if we felt like a movie. We found a large washtub for him and organized a relay team, while I myself limited my activities to offering technical advice and maintaining the pace.

* * *

By eight in the evening we were alone with our flood again, The Seligs broke down first, then Zvika collapsed in the garden, and we had to let them go. We decided not to rely on miracles again and drew up a list of our acquaintances, ticking off those we knew to be in good physical shape.

"I believe Weinreb plays tennis," the woman said pensively, "and he's got this big hefty wife . . ."

The Weinrebs were a little surprised at our warm invitation, so sudden too, and anyhow, they were expecting this tourist couple who'd just come from Chile.

"Your friends are our friends," the little one declared solemnly, "Bring them too . . ."

So they came, our new team, Weinreb with his table-tennis

135

bats in case I felt like a game. Little did he know. Because guess what had suddenly happened?

I went over our flood story again, very tired now, on account of having had to shave and change into dry clothes every time a new shift came on, to lend my story credence. Our visitors were extremely sympathetic and set to work at once, cheered on by me:

"Heave ho!" I cried, to keep up the rhythm, "Heave ho! . . ."

The Chilean couple were particularly good at the job, reaching an output of some two cubic yds. an hour, and what with Weinreb being such a tennis champ, they managed to get the water down again to three inches. Then the wife, overcome with *hubris,* committed her blunder:

"Oh dear," she said, "How you must hate us. Working yourself to death on our account. Most people I know would have gone right back home . . ."

She and her big mouth. The four of them downed their tools and went right back home. That's friendship for you: comes your hour of need – they desert you. The trouble was that by then we'd got so used to the slave labour system that we didn't know how to cope any more and just sat there watching the steadily rising tide in helpless dismay. Five minutes later I resolved on action and rang up Meir Geiger, because he lives near and would be able to get to us fast. Yona, his wife, came to the phone.

"We'd love to come," she said, "but our car's stuck in the mud."

"So come on foot, it's only round the corner. And bring a deck of cards . . ."

"On foot? It's raining. Know something? Come pick us up in your car."

"Splendid! I'm on my way!"

Afraid of getting wet, the spoilt bitch. I left my little Dutchwoman to her dyke, raced round the corner to the Geigers, swept up to their doorstep and wanted to turn on my heel at once – but too late. Yona had been watching out for me.

"You can't imagine what's just happened," she whispered out of breath, "A minute ago our cellar . . ."

I'd fallen into the trap like a baby. Pick us up in your car, huh? The mean double-crossing rats! I was so furious at those two that I deliberately spilled water on their best rug every time I came up with my buckets. What the hell, here I was bailing out the Geiger Lake with the last of my strength, and at home my own wife was up to her knees in our own Waterloo . . .

In the end the Lord delivered us, as usual. The windows of heaven were stopped, as it says in Genesis, and the waters abated, and seedtime and harvest and cold and heat, and something something summer and winter, and lo, the Weinrebs met the Geigers and Zvika and the tourist couple, and now they don't speak to us any longer, selah.

Sink or Swim

My son stands on the edge of the swimming pool, crying.
"Amir, come on in!"
"I'm scared."
I know he is. I've been spending the past half hour trying
to coax my little redhead to let Daddy teach him to swim, but
he's scared. He's crying too, softly as yet, in low gear so to
say, but steadily, and with a hint of better to come. I'm not
angry with him. I remember my own father trying to teach
me to swim, and me, too, standing at the edge of the pool and
being scared. Educational methods have changed, though:
me, I don't intend to force my boy. No, he'll have to take
the first step in his conquest of the waves of his own free will.
Like a young eagle, say, leaving the nest for the first time
– he'll only need a little push, and Nature will do the rest,
however badly. All that's called for on my part is patience,
understanding, and love – love above all.
"Look," I tell my little fledgling, "the water'll only come
up to your belly-button, that's all, and I'll be holding you
like this, see?"
"I'm scared"
"All the other kids are in the water, laughing and having
fun, and only you are crying. Why're you crying?"
"I'm scared."
"But why? You're no dumber than other kids, are you?"
"Yes!"
This last comes out with great conviction, by way of
summing up. I look round: the lifeguard is watching me from

138

under the brim of his straw hat, the other kids' parents are grinning. I picture a sinking ship. Everybody on board waits for the Captain's instructions, and only one man, a huge redhead, pushes his way past the women and children and jumps into the lifeboat — my son, whose father didn't teach him to swim . . .

"What're you scared of?"

"I'll sink."

"You *can't* sink in a little bit of water like that. You don't sink in the bathtub, do you?"

"I'm scared."

The little land-rat.

"You couldn't sink if you wanted to." I try an appeal to reason, "The body's specific gravity is lower than that of the water, see, so it floats! Here, watch!"

Daddy lies on the water and floats for all he's worth. Very instructive, except that just then some idiot takes it into his head to dive bang on top of me. My mouth fills with water, I splutter and go down, specific gravity and all. My son's crying goes into high.

I decide to enlist the help of the Authorities. "Mr. Lifeguard," I say, "You tell this little boy: can anyone drown in the kids' pool?"

"Oh, yes," says Straw-Hat, "They can and they have."

Another daddy would long ago have thrown his son in, but not me. Me, I'm fond of my son, little coward though he is. Nay, I love him *because* he's such a little coward, so small, so lost, so helpless . . .

"Know what?" I say, "Let's make a deal. I won't touch you, and you'll go in all by yourself. Just go in up to your knees. You like it — you stay. You don't — you get out and that's it. What say?"

Amir cries, but edges off the edge. Result: he *doesn't* like it, *doesn't* stay, gets out and that's it. He's back on dry land, and crying on a note of outraged virtue. "Mummy!" he cries, "Mu-hu-my!" It's one of those weird habits children have, to call on their mummies for help in every situation, even if mummy is chasing them round the table with a rolling-pin right then.

"Amir," I point out, "Either you get into this pool now, or no television for a week."

Have I gone too far? Amir can cry in reverse too. The water in the pool is getting all salty.

"It's so easy," I tell him, demonstrating, "You stretch your arms like this and just count: one, two, three . . . four . . ."

All right, so I can't both swim *and* count. I'm not a professional, dammit. I gasp for breath, and Amir gets scareder and scareder. We've already attracted quite a little crowd in search of entertainment. I leap out of the pool and my boy runs for his life, crying at top pitch, but in vain – I seize him and drag him to the water by his hairs: he'll swim of his own free will if it's the last thing he does.

"Mu-hu-my," he cries, "Sca-ha-red!"

It all seems very familiar suddenly. Ah, I know, my father dragged me to the pool just like this and I too yelled bloody murder. Well, that's how it is, there's no avoiding the generation clash, the fathers eat sour grapes and the children yell bloody murder.

"No!" he yells, "No! Mummy!"

I'm holding him in the air a yard above water and he claims he's drowning.

"One, two, three," I command, *"Swim!"*

He cries but moves his arms, which is fine, but I'm not teaching him to fly, am I? I lower my little eagle down to water level. He fights for his life, swears, tries to wriggle out of my grasp but I'm stronger than he is.

"Swim!" I thunder at him, "One, two, three . . ."

He's bitten me! Bitten the hand that feeds him – on water just now, but still. I catch him between my legs and grip his trembling body in a steel vice. I take hold of his hands and push them forwards and back, and one, and two, and three, he'll swim if he has to drink up the whole pool . . . "Shut up and swim. SWIM!"

One day he'll be grateful for this, but right now he kicks.

His feet kick against my back in a steady tattoo, keeping time with his screams. His face is all twisted with crying, he's aged a whole day in an hour. I push him well under. He's drinking a little water? He can drink a whole ocean! So did my father when my grandfather taught him to swim. Swim, you brat! It's been ages since I've been so furious at anyone. Scared! What's there to be scared of, dammit!

"Mister," says the lifeguard, tapping me on the shoulder, "Please let go of that child."

There! Instead of helping a father teach his son, instead of giving him a hand, a swimming belt, something, he comes to the aid of the screaming minority. I pick my eagle up and put him to shore with unconcealed contempt. Amir stands at the edge and cries like he's never cried before. I leap back into the water.

I do a graceful swan dive to show the little fool what he's missing, start out on a fast breast stroke, but something's wrong . . . it's as if my legs won't keep pace with my arms, as if I'm sinking . . . I *am* sinking . . . Help! . . . Mu-hu-my! . . . One swimming lesson, and already I've forgotten how to swim.

The Forsyte Saga

"Who's that?" I asked, "Is that the guy that pinched books off of Fleur's husband?"

"No, stupid," said my wife, "That's Winifred's nephew."

"Him that fell off the horse?"

"No, that was Frances, June's mother, shhh!"

It used to be the same every Friday night, all during those heady months when Israeli TV was showing us the Saga that Conquered the World: Forsyte. We'd sit glued to the screen, along with Amir who ought to have been in bed, and I always forgot who was who. Like I spend an average evening thinking that this painter who's doing the nude is the son of that woman, Lady Whatsit, till Amir explains that no, he's old Jolyon's cousin, shhh!

Why don't they run the names on top like in the news? There, now Fleur's husband is making a speech in the House, and I don't remember whether he's Irene's son or not, *if* it's Irene whom Soames raped five instalments back. To make matters worse, there's Renana, our new baby daughter, and she's making a funny sort of noise and crying. Could she have climbed over the bars of her crib and be playing dangerous games now? Or is she just doing a little balancing act on top of the bar? The cold sweat breaks out on my forehead. The little woman is squirming in her chair too.

"Who's that?" I ask, "Is that the one who has a crush on Fleur?"

Somewhere in the house the phone goes, but we don't move. Anyone who calls up in the middle of Forsyte can't be in his right mind anyhow. Three Fridays ago somebody rang at the door, a telegram or what, and he kept his finger on the bell for ten minutes, but we couldn't open because Soames was just having it out with Irene about June's engagement or something.

"Quiet!" I yelled at the door, "Forsyte!"

Crash! The sound of a falling baby comes from Renana's room, followed by loud wails. She's dropped out of her crib, our little girl, I'm sure she has.

"Amir," I snap at my son, "Go and see what's happened. Hurry!"

"What for?" mutters my son, "She's already fallen anyway . . ."

There, that's what it's come to — a TV show is more important to him than his sister! The wife is worried sick. Soames is arguing with some youngster — a lawyer, I think.

"Who's that?" I asked, "Is that Helen's son?"

"Shhhhh!"

Renana seemed to have picked herself up and moved on to our bedroom: sounds of heavy furniture being shifted and shattering glass. No, I thought, this lawyer can't be Helen's son. Helen's son was killed in a road accident. Or no, that wasn't him but Bosinney, the architect. Fell under a carriage or something.

"Then who's that?" I asked, "Could that be Marjorie's brother, by any chance?"

"She hasn't got a brother," the little one hissed, "Look to your right!"

I waited for a switch of scenes, then shot a rapid glance sideways. A man was standing quietly beside my armchair, his face disguised under a nylon stocking, a large bag slung over his shoulder. Michael, Fleur's husband, was being beaten up by someone in the House. Not the House proper. The loo.

"Who's that bugger that's hitting him?" the man with the bag asked, "Isn't that Winifred's husband?"

"Pooh! Winifred's husband ran off to America with that actress woman ages ago," I said, "Shhh!"

143

That wretched Soames was in trouble again: the young lawyer was bleeding him white.

"What that poor man's got to go through," the little one sighed, "Everybody has it in for him."

"Don't you feel sorry for that bastard," someone on my other side said, "Remember the way he treated Irene on their wedding night, who's that?"

"Shhh!"

By now I could see *two* men with bags standing there.

"Sit down!" I said, "I can't see!"

The two lowered themselves to the carpet.

"What's going on?" the wife asked, "Who're those?"

"Ann's brother," one of our visitors answered, "John's second wife. Shhh!"

The two of them started whispering to each other, which was a nuisance, so the wife made signals for me to do something, but I was waiting for some sort of break. It came with the maid of Soames' sister's cousin, who was a bit of a bore and could be skipped. I rushed to the kitchen and rang the Police. It took three minutes before an impatient voice answered:

"The sergeant's busy. Call back at 10.50."

"Wait!" I roared, "I've got two burglars in my living room."

"Caught in Forsyte?"

"Yes, Send someone fast."

"In a while," said the duty cop, "Who's that?"

I gave him my name.

"I didn't mean you," said the cop and hung up.

I rushed back to the Saga.

"What did I miss?" I asked, "Isn't that whosit, Holly's brother?"

"What's the matter with you?" the tallest of the burglars said, "Holly's brother died of typhus in the *first* instalment, for God's sake."

"Ah, then this is the cousin of that Red . . ."

"Blue-blue-blue . . ."

That was Renana, who'd crawled all the way from her

room to my armchair like a big girl. A police siren came screaming up the street. One of the burglars half got up, but just then Marjorie walked into the hospital and met Fleur face to face beside whatsisname's bed. The suspense was hardly bearable. Someone was raining blows on our front door.

"Who's that?" I asked, "Is that the one that went to Australia?"

"No, that was Irene's stepfather, shhh!"

The front door fell in and we were vaguely conscious of some uniformed figures slipping into the room and lining up along the wall behind our backs.

"Who's that?" asked one of the cops, "Isn't that Holly's husband — Val's wife?"

"Shut up!"

In the end Fleur refused to make it up with Marjorie and went off to nurse Ann's brother, to be continued next week. It had been a great instalment.

"I don't think Fleur is right," the sergeant observed, "I mean, so long as Marjorie made this gesture, she should have let bygones be bygones. And at her brother's death-bed too!"

"Come off it, Marjorie's just trying to blackmail her," said one of our burglars from the door, "And anyhow, he's not her brother. He's Vic's husband, him that hired the dicks."

"Nuts!" I called after them, "That one left for the Far East two Fridays back."

"That, if you don't mind, was Wilfred, the poet," my wife corrected me, "Won't you ever learn to keep them apart?"

Really, as if I had nothing else to worry about. She herself had for two whole instalments thought like a fool that this chap with the balloons who went to fight the Boers was Jolyon Jr. It's not from her I'll learn my Forsyte, I'm sure.

Patsy

Renana is growing fast. She's out of her diapers already, though still addicted to the pacifier. Our doctor says not to worry, all babies cling to their pacifiers in the interval between their last bottle and their first cigarette. According to him pacifiers are just a mother substitute, though most mothers I know aren't made of pink plastic with yellow rubber in the middle. Still, as long as the doctor says it's normal . . .

The only thing that does worry us is that with Renana it isn't just any old pacifier – it's one specific pacifier, by name of Patsy.

To us adults Patsy is a perfectly ordinary pacifier, a plain mass product of the baby industry, but it's a fact that our daughter refuses to touch any other. Whenever we try slipping one of Patsy's doubles past her, she spits it out in disgust after the first mouthful and starts screaming, kicking the furniture, throwing things about, stepping on the dog's tail and shouting. Like Amir, she's a redhead.

"Patsy!" she screams, "Patsy! Pat-seeeee! . . ."

Of course we've all been down on our hands and knees from the first "Patsy", hunting feverishly for the lost treasure. Anyone who finds Patsy feels like Columbus at the cry of "Land!" because then Renana calms down at once and falls to sucking contentedly, while we slump about her, exhausted.

"It's a sign," says our doctor, "that the child lacks parental love."

That's a lie, because we love Renana very much, as long as she doesn't scream. It all depends on Patsy. We have Patsy –

146

we have peace. We haven't — we haven't. Whenever we spend an evening at some friends', the wife goes cold when the phone rings, lest it's the babysitter to say she can't find Patsy and Renana is going purple in the face. When that happens we race home over the dead bodies of a dozen traffic cops and find a frantic sitter turning the house upside down in quest of the runaway Patsy.

"Oh dear," the little woman sighs from time to time, "if ever Patsy gets lost . . ."

It's something that doesn't bear thinking on, like nuclear war. What really beats us is: how does Renana know that Patsy is Patsy?

One day I stole out of the house with the sacred pacifier and took it to the pharmacy I'd bought it at. I asked for exactly the same again, same colour, same size, even the same year of make on the assumption that, like vintage wines, pacifiers too might have their good and bad years. The same pharmacist gave me the same pacifier, I put it in the same pocket and went home through the same streets.

The fake Patsy sailed through the room:

"This not Patsy!"

*   *   *

My wife thinks it's the wear and tear that make the difference. To be sure, Patsy's rubber part has — if you'll pardon me — gone green with rot. Maybe that's what gives it its special flavour, but you should have seen the pharmacist's face when I asked did she sell used pacifiers. So then we decided to do our own decaying in an improvised home lab. We bought some prussic acid and stuff, and put a few guinea-pig pacifiers to soak in the solution, and the rubber greened to a nice olive shade but remained quite unsuckable. Renana saw through our game with her first lick . . .

The doctor prescribed a tranquillizer, so we bought a big bottle of Atarax and even that did no good. There was, for instance, the night our babysitter rang up in a panic and we rushed home to find that Patsy had disappeared from the special nail we would hang it on every morning.

"Patsy!" the little woman moaned, "Someone's nabbed it!"

Our first suspicion fell on the milkman but he denied it hotly. So did Rafi, Amir, the help, the postman, and Felix Selig, and we were just about to phone Gramps who'd also been in the house that day, when Patsy turned up in the springs of our second-best armchair.

"But how on earth did it *get* there?" said the wife, raising her eyes to heaven, "Dear God, how?"

We asked Stucks the plumber whether he knew of a special Geiger counter or something to detect hidden pacifiers with, and he said no, but why didn't we get us a dog from the Drug Squad instead, they could sniff out anything. Someone else suggested one of those tiny transmitters pilots have, which go blip-blip when the pilot bails out. It seemed like a good idea – but how attach it to Patsy? The most practical thing of all would have been simply to chain Patsy to the cot, but our doctor disapproved:

"The child might strangle herself," he said, "Just give her more love."

"Ephraim," the little one warned me, "I feel I'm going out of my mind."

She started having these terrible nightmares too. She'd dream that an anteater had come in through the kitchen, grabbed Patsy and run off to the deepest African jungle, and she'd never find it again, the more as she didn't know what an anteater was exactly. She also kept fancying that The Pacifier was escaping all by itself, like in those cartoons on TV: hop-hop-hop, and Patsy is over the wall . . . Appalling!

And then we discovered Patsy's dark secret.

The evening began as usual: at seven o'clock the woman crossed to our new steel safe, inserted her key, turned the lock and removed Patsy. Then she put Renana to bed, popped Patsy in, went out and locked the door. At that time Patsy was insured for 20,000 pounds. Not that money could have made up for the loss of one disgusting, sickly green pacifier, but still . . .

Then I rose and peeked through the keyhole.

"Woman," I called softly, "Come here!"

What we saw through the keyhole was our little Renana slipping quietly out of bed, going to the sofa and pushing Patsy well down into the upholstery. Then she toddled back, climbed into her cot and started screaming . . .

We heaved a sigh of relief: so the child was fit as a flea, had no complexes whatever, was not in love with any pacifier, but was simply tormenting us for the fun of it. Our doctor said this was fairly common with children her age, and probably indicated a lack of parental love. He prescribed another bottle of Atarax but to no effect — the little woman and I had got used to the stuff by then.

High Jinks

Renana is a dear child. There's something positive about her. It's still hard to tell positively what, but there is. There *must* be. Anyway, while other infants put everything in their mouths, step on things and smash them, Renana never applies force to anything she lays her hands on but simply throws it out through the railings of our second-floor balcony. Every day at noon when I come home I spend some time picking up the dumb objects littering the pavement in front of our house. Sometimes the neighbours give a hand and collect the books, salt cellars, fountain pens, ashtrays, cutlery, transistors, records gone to glory, shoes, clocks, typewriters and other surprises. They, the neighbours, ring at our door with armfuls of fall-out and ask:

"Why do you give these things to Baby?"

We give'em, huh? As if Baby couldn't take them herself. She's a very well developed child, our Renana is. The line on the doorpost − with the pencil held at a slight angle − has reached a high-water mark of 28 inches, and it doesn't need much to figure out that her raised hands can reach anything in the region of 37 in.

"Ephraim," said the little woman therefore, "the danger zone is just under a yard . . ."

And that's where our standard of living began to rise.

In one lightning operation all the glass and china in the living room was transferred to the piano. The lower shelves of the book-case were evacuated and the refugees took to the hills. Our crystal fruit-bowl was awarded supreme status on top of the cupboard. Shoes were stuck in among the linen. My papers were carefully heaped up in the centre of my writing desk, so that Renana's roving hands got only as far as bare table-edge and stopped short of balcony-literature.

"Ho-ho," we grinned at our offspring with a hint of mockery, "Nothing more to throw now, huh?"

Renana grit her teeth and resolutely started to grow. She's like old Darwin's giraffe which was obliged to lengthen its neck in order to reach the treetops. Our daughter, too, was straining up, up, up – till after a couple of weeks only a mere inch or two divided her from the closet keys (one yd., three in.)

"Ephraim," said the child's mama, "if she reaches the keys I'm moving out . . ."

She always moves out as soon as anything goes wrong, though I admit the future did look bleak. We were particularly sensitive about the phone, which had always stood peacefully on its own little table. It was a pretty sturdy little table too, but below the Olympic minimum. Renana toddled over to it in a moment of leisure, pulled the instrument down to floor level and yelled into the ruins:

"Allo! Allo! Allo!"

Her mother leaped swiftly into the fray, grabbed Renana, spanked her behind and shouted over and over:

"Na, na, na! Mustn't touch phone! Not phone! Na, na!"

As a result, our bright child stopped yelling "Allo! Allo!" into the ruins and switched to "Nanana!" Since that didn't seem much of an improvement, I took several fat volumes of encyclopaedia, A to C, and placed them under the phone to raise its level of reception. I'll never forget the effect of that hasty step, which occurred one hot day when I came home and tripped over "Aardvark-Barcelona" on the pavement. I realized in a flash that the phone must be out of order . . .

And sure enough, I found my wife mourning over a graveyard of splinters:

"It's the end," she whispered with unseeing eyes, "Renana uses pillows."

Baby, that is, had all on her own discovered Jefferson's Law which says that "a body rises in direct proportion to the object placed under her feet". For the time being she only used the sofa pillows: two of them, she found, would elevate her to the lofty peak of one yd., 21 in. . . . .

Na-na-na, our standard of living was rising again.

Stationery and precious manuscripts went to the mini-concentration camp on the piano. Keys were hung on special nails in the stratosphere to be safe from our pillow-fighter. The radio broadcast at us hi-fi and dry from the cupboard roof, and our creepers crept along the curtain-rods like the hanging gardens of Babylon. Nevertheless, the boy we had hired to pick up our treasures from the pavement would still tug at the rope about once every 15 minutes as a sign for us to haul up a basketful of missiles. Life became rather complicated. Our entire household was piled up on the pianoforte, and in order to make a phone call from the wardrobe one had to get up on the tea trolley . . .

"Good gracious," sighed the wife one sleepless night, "what'll it be like in a few years . . ."

I suppose Renana will grow up to be a basketball player. Anyhow, next day at noon I met my neighbour Felix Selig outside with a watercolour round his neck. This work of art happens to portray an Israeli harbour in delicate pinks and mauves, and Selig's head was sticking right through the hull of a freighter. He was speechless. The balcony's on the *second* floor.

"Yes," I said, "Baby's growing."

Inside I found the remnants of my wife pale as a sheet: "Ephraim," she whispered, "she . . . climbs . . . chairs . . ."

The child, that is, had now discovered Hegel's Law of Progress by Stages and had translated it all by herself into progress by stairs: she had got up on a pillow, from the pillow to the edge of the sewing case, from there onto a chair, and from the chair on our nerves. Our standard of living had thereby risen to such dizzy heights that I guess only the U.S.A. can match it: 5 ft., 3 in.!

For a start, my writing desk went up to the piano. This piece, for example, is being written at an altitude of six feet about carpet-level. True, my head touches the ceiling, but the air up here is bracing. A person can get used to anything, and children fill one's life with a variety of it. Phone calls are made from the top rung of a ladder bought for the purpose. We dine on the wardrobe-roof in the clouds. They say it's a very healthy way of life: back to the trees. We're gradually learning to walk on the ceiling . . . Renana is growing.

Na-na-na.

Last night the wife, ironing clothes somewhere in the highlands, gave a stifled cry:

"Ephraim!" – with a trembling finger she pointed at Renana down below – "Look!"

Baby was climbing the ladder, step by evolutionary step. That did it. It's been a good life, nice to've met you, but there are limits. I refuse to be a poet with my head perpetually in the clouds. I've asked my wife to write and let me know when Renana's grown up. Till then I'm floored.

Maximalism

One happy day Renana threw Patsy through the balcony
railings and the fall killed her, whereupon Renana went off
pacifiers altogether, and I was just thinking our troubles were
over when the little woman decided that the kids wanted
a dog.

"Hell," I said, "Not again. I thought we'd gone into all
that."

"Just by way of trial," thus the woman, "For the kids'
sake."

"Yeah. And then we get attached to it and we're stuck . . ."

Next the wife talked to the kids, with the result that Amir
and Renana came and sat on my knee and started going –
daddydogdaddydogdaddydog. I resolved to meet them
halfway:

"All right," I said, "A dog. What kind?"

"A thoroughbred," said my wife, "Pedigreed."

I realized at once she'd been consulting some of the dog-
owners in the neighbourhood. Now I also understood the
meaning of the malicious grins I'd caught on their faces when
they looked at me.

"I don't want one of those large beasts that'll wreck the
house," my wife continued with her briefing, "nor a little one
either – they're silly. It shouldn't be too young, on account of
the house-training. Or too old. Old dogs have asthma. That's
why pedigree is so important, to make sure it's got pink jaws,
straight legs, and straight hair. I don't want a curly dog. So
listen, get us one that's obedient, that's got a good clear bark

154

but is quiet, and doesn't bite or chew the carpets, and *not* a bitch, because they're in heat every so often. Better don't get a male either because they're always chasing bitches. And of course not one that costs a fortune, but a real thoroughbred with a proper lineage and all, because only those are worth the money you pay for them . . ."

"Right," I said, "If you're sure that's what the kids want . . ."

"Yes. Off you go, and remember — keep your eyes open and *don't* just buy the first dog they offer you . . ."

* * *

I put on my coat and set out for town with my eyes open. On the way I popped into the post office for stamps and found myself queuing up behind a man with a bad cough, who saw the thoughtful expression on my face and asked was I looking for a dog, and he had one in his garden, which was just round the corner from the post office. I went with him. The dog turned out to be a small puppy with curly hair, bow-legs, and one of those black noses with lots of pink spots. It lay in an old shoebox and chewed on its tail, but when it saw us it jumped up and began licking my ankles with gusto. I promptly became attached to it.

"What's its name?" I asked.

"Dunno," said the man with a cough, "You want it?"

"Is it a thoroughbred?"

"A thoroughbred?" the man flared up, "Listen, chum, this dog is the product of some dozen different breeds, and if that isn't thorough I don't know what is. It's a dog, it barks, what more do you want? So are you taking it or aren't you?"

He was getting impatient so I said yes. I'd got attached to the animal too, as I said.

"How much do you want for him?"

"Nothing. Just take it away."

He wrapped the mongrel in a newspaper, thrust it into my hands and shoved us out, but before I'd walked very far I remembered my wife and stopped dead in my tracks. This — it flashed through my mind — this wasn't exactly the dog

155

we'd been talking of only ten minutes back. No, and if I showed up with it we'd both be kicked down the stairs. I took another look at my acquisition; it lay there shivering slightly, with only its tip sticking out of the bad news. The tip, I now saw, actually was a *pink* nose with *black* spots. No, this wouldn't get by at home. I'd need to prepare the ground first. I'd need time.

I hurried back to Mr. Cough.

"I'm not going home right now," I lied, "I'll pick him up in the afternoon or sometime."

"Look," said Mr. Cough, "I'm willing to pay you a couple of quid . . ."

"No, no, I'm attached to him already. I'll come back, don't worry."

* * *

"Well?" the woman asked, "Found something?"

Did she really think I'd fall for that?

"My dear," I said, frowning at her, "You don't buy a dog the way you'd buy a pound of apples! I did see a few Scotch terriers and a Settler, but their pedigree looked rather shaky to me . . ."

I wasn't quite sure if there was such a thing as "Settler," but it sounded good. Come to that, what did pedigree mean exactly? Race? Breed? Something to do with feet, like pedicure?

The little woman, in any case, was satisfied: I was working on the dog, I wasn't going to buy the first mongrel that came my way. She approved.

"You're right," she said, "Easy does it. We don't buy a dog every day, after all."

"Uh-huh," thus I, "I've seen some ads in the paper. I guess I'll put out some feelers tomorrow."

* * *

Next morning I went straight to the beach and swam and sunbathed and watched the bikini-parade till noon. On the way home I paid a brief call on my puppy in the garden. He was very happy to see me and licked me all over, and I

156

noticed there was something funny about his tongue as well. It was sort of crooked. This puppy obviously hadn't got a drop of blue blood in him. I was mad to think I'd get away with it.

"Tomorrow," I told Cough, "First thing in the morning. We're all getting anti-rabies shots tomorrow, so the day after we'll be ready for him . . ."

* * *

"Those ads aren't worth the paper they're printed on," I complained to my wife. "You've no idea the number of mixed breeds they've been trying to pass off on me today."

"Still," the wife said, and I could hear the faint note of suspicion in her voice, "Still, what exactly did you see?" She forgot I'm a poet or what?

"I saw quite a tolerable Yorkshire poodle in Ramat Gan," I told her pensively, "but his certificates only went back four generations. I also had the impression there'd been a case or two of incest in the family."

"What do you expect?" thus the woman, "That's quite normal with dogs."

"But not with *me!* With me it's all or nothing, and when I say pedigree I mean pedigree!"

I can rise to the occasion as well as anyone.

The little woman looked up at me with an unfamiliar expression in her eyes. Respect, was it? Admiration?

"You are so right," she breathed, "And me thinking you'd go and get us the first mongrel you saw . . ."

"Charming!" I said angrily, "Here we've been married 12 years, and that's how much you know about me! Well, just for your information, I'm going all the way to Haifa tomorrow to consult Dr. Menczel. Yes, *the* Dr. Menczel, the country's foremost expert on dogenealogy . . ."

Next morning I took the car, parked it behind the post office and went to the garden to see Max, who fairly jumped into my arms with joy when I tiptoed over to his shoebox. I decided to teach him a few tricks like jumping hurdles and catching thieves and such, but he proved a slow learner. For

157

a minute I even felt sorry I'd become so attached to him. On top of it Cough suddenly showed up and started yelling that he'd throw the bloody animal out into the street if I didn't take her away at once.

"Please," I asked, "Did you say *her?*"

"Him, her, what's the difference?" said that idiot, "Just take the bitch away now!"

Max, too, gave me a questioning look and nearly wagged her tail off:

"Nu?" said her eyes, "Why aren't we going?"

"I'm working on it," I signalled back, "I'm working on it."

* * *

At home I sank into a chair, tired to death after my long drive.

"I saw Dr. Menczel," I reported, "and she did show me some fairly handsome animals. But pure? All the way? Somehow I felt a sort of nagging doubt, a tiny . . ."

"Aren't you being a bit too fastidious?" the little one interrupted me, "Nobody's perfect, you know."

"I don't care," I told her firmly, "I'm not taking any second-best, and that's flat. Actually I've decided to order a really noble animal from abroad. I've heard of this famous kennel in Switzerland . . ."

"How much will it cost, though?"

"Don't ask! I've already picked one too — an off-white miniature schnauzer that goes right back to Frederick the Great on his father's side, and to Excellenz von der Stuchholz on his mother's. A true colour-blind aristocrat."

"Good," said the wife a bit wearily, "fine."

The next three days were the hardest of all my shuttle-diplomacy. I told Cough I wanted Max to be a birthday present for my little girl, so could he keep her for just a few more days. He said nothing, just grabbed Max and threw her after me over the fence. I took her in my arms, scratched her ears to cheer her up a bit, then threw her back into the garden and ran.

"I've asked them to keep Max at the airport for a day," I

informed my wife, "while I have his biography checked by the Veterinary Institute in Jerusalem."

"You're getting to be a proper snob," the woman muttered, but I could see her resistance had crumbled. Next morning I found Max waiting for me on a street corner, whimpering pathetically. The heartless brute had turned her out of house and garden between two coughing fits. I bought the poor little thing a nice new collar with lots of brass studs, and took her home.

"Straight from Switzerland," I introduced her, "Max."

The family looked at her in awe: a real Swiss miniature schnauzer, bursting with pedigree, a prince among dogs.

"Nice," said the wife, "Cute. Really worth waiting for."

There, she'd already got attached to it. She *is* nice, though, is our Max. Her tail wags like a metronome, and her eyes shine with so much intelligence you sometimes feel she may start speaking at any moment. Personally I'd rather she kept mum.

Max's School Days

It didn't take long for Max to settle in, and by now she has us well in hand. It starts with the early-morning inspection, when she leaps up on our beds, gives us a good licking, then turns to chew up the bedclothes. In the short time she's been with us, our miniature schnauzer bitch has already devoured a dozen slippers, a rug or two, a transistor radio and two thrillers. When she started on my desk, however, I decided to put an end to it and banished her to the backyard; since when she hasn't been allowed into the house again, except by day and by night.

"Ephraim," said the little woman therefore, "Do you think we're bringing her up properly?"

I had a few doubts on the subject myself. Our thoroughbred mongrel spends most of her free time sprawling on the softest of our armchairs. She wags her tail happily at every stranger who comes to the door, and only barks when the little woman starts playing the piano. On top of that the children stuff her with chocolate and cookies, so that rather than a miniature schnauzer she looks like a baby hippo. She also uses the living-room carpet to pee on — and worse. All in all I daresay she's a wee bit spoilt.

"Listen," I said to the wife, "How if we sent her to school?"

I'd got the idea from watching Zulu, a black shepherd that walks past our windows twice a day, close on the heels of Dragomir the dog-trainer.

"Heel!" Dragomir barks from time to time, "Down! Git!"

And that big dumb animal obeys him like a machine, and sits, gits and finds on command. Shameful, that's what it is.

"He's turning that poor beast into a robot," the little woman declared, "A regular soulless robot."

We looked back at Max, our own Max busily tearing up a hand-embroidered cushion to see what was inside, and oozing soul all over the place. And last night she'd done Worse right in the middle of the living room again.

"Ah, well," said the woman with downcast eyes, "Maybe you should see this Dragomir after all."

This Dragomir is a hefty fellow in the prime of life who understands dog language like Wise King Solomon in his heyday. He's rather less fluent in human languages, though I hear he speaks his native Croatian well enough.

"What dis?" Dragomir asked when I presented Max to him, "Where you gets dis?"

"Never mind that now," I said, slightly offended, "The point is – she's here, and we'd like you to train her."

Dragomir grabbed Max by the scruff of the neck, raised her to the level of his face, and looked right through her.

"How you feeds dog?"

I told him soup, roast beef and noodles, with strawberries for dessert. Also jam, cream puffs, or popcorn, whenever she felt like a snack.

"Bad," thus Dragomir, "Dog to gets food only once time a day – and stops. Where dog embowels?"

"In the house," I basely informed on her. "On the carpet. Never in the garden. I wonder why that is?"

"I tells you: dog always embowels in same spot where he dones first time, on account of smell," explained the great man, "How many often he dones in house?"

I did a little sum in my head: Max misbehaves about once every two hours, so in three months that would come to . . .

"Something like 500 times."

"Good gods!" Dragomir exclaimed, "Must sells dis dog."

He explained why. It seems that in only three months we'd managed to persuade Max that our garden was her house,

161

and our house her john.

"Please do something," I begged Dragomir, "Try and save her. I'll pay anything!"

"First all, you ties up dog," the trainer ordered, "I gets you strong chain."

Max looked at Dragomir adoringly and wagged her tail like mad. Who ever said little dogs are smart?

Next day Dragomir turned up with a heavy iron chain — pinched from a ship or something — broke our broomstick over his knee, stuck it in the ground at the far end of the garden, and chained up our little Max.

"So," he declared, "Stays like so all de time. Once time a day he eats a little. Nobody goes near her."

Our hearts bled.

"But she'll cry," I protested feebly, "She's used to having people round her. She'll cry . . ."

"Lets her," thus Dragomir the Dragon, "I not allows no pootshie-mootshie."

An intimidating sort of person, this Dragomir, but with heaps of authority. I didn't like him all the same. His teeth were yellow, for one thing.

He was flashing them at me now, trying to persuade me once again that it would be easier for all concerned if we sold Max. She wasn't a miniature schnauzer anyhow, he argued, but a miniature schnorrer at best, so why waste good money on her. I swore by all that's holy that we would obey his instructions to the letter, do whatever he told us to do, only please let him not take her away from us.

"Kay," he agreed, "So 1,500 pound now here."

Max started to howl in her fetters. She'd noticed something at last.

By that afternoon we were all howling. The kids saw Max pining away in her garden exile, and their hearts went out to her. So miserable she looked, so lonely, so betrayed. In the end Renana ran out sobbing and lay down on the ground beside Max in a show of solidarity. Amir, who is older and wiser, kept at me to release the dog just for a little, but I stood pat:

"Sorry," I said, "I have my instructions."

"Just for ten minutes," the little woman pleaded, "Five minutes, then."

In the end I softened. All right, five minutes and not a second more. Max tore into the house like a Prometheus unbound and nearly licked the skin off us. She spent the night in Amir's bed, snuggled under the blanket with him, being fed on raisins and shoes. In the morning Dragomir rang up:

"How is dog night?"

"Kay," I said, "Fine. Swell."

"She barks?"

"Let her barks."

Max was crouched on my chest, cocking an ear at the phone and toying with my glasses. Dragomir explained once again how absolutely vital it was to stick to the rules, especially at first, keep Max tied up, feed her once a day, and not go near her, not go near.

"Sure," I said, "Absolutely. Look, Mr. Dragomir, I spend a fortune on this dog's education, I'm not going to louse it up with my own hands, am I?"

Dragomir saw the point and was satisfied. I hung up, removed the phone-cord from between Max's teeth, and sat down to work with a sigh of relief.

Around noon Amir burst into the house panting:

"Quick!" he shouted, "Dragomir!"

We snatched Max off the piano, rushed out into the garden with her and tied her up with the anchor chain. By the time the trainer arrived, we were all sitting round the table, virtuously eating our dinner.

"Where dog?" asked Dragomir.

"Well where?" thus the wife, "In the garden where she belongs."

"Good," he said, "No lets free."

Never, we said, what did he take us for, and we duly kept Max in irons till he left, when we let her back in for the pudding. Max was delighted, if confused. She couldn't quite understand this novel regime of being grabbed and tied to the stake whenever that big dragon man showed up, and being returned to her loo again as soon as he left. It worked, though, and after a week or so she got used to it and would run into the garden herself the moment she heard Dragomir coming. As for me, I derived a lot of creative satisfaction from dreaming up my daily progress reports for Dragomir's benefit. The day Max pulled the cloth off the table, dishes and all, we even raised his salary to ease our conscience.

And then Dragomir made the mistake of his life. He came in the evening.

It was Zulu again who started it: he'd bitten the postman in the leg, and Dragomir had been called up to give Zulu a talking-to. Then he figured that as long as he was in the neighbourhood, he might as well drop in on us too. He visited the garden, turned and walked in through the kitchen door, and continued right on to the children's room. There he found Max in Amir's arms, the two of them sitting on the bed, watching TV and munching peanuts.

"Dis you calls garden?" Dragomir roared, "Dis you calls tied up?"

"Sorry," said Amir and ducked under the blanket, "We weren't expecting you . . ."

I myself fled to the bathroom, jumped under the shower and started singing at the top of my voice. The little woman, however, sprouted wings and soared:

"To hell with your garden!" she yelled right into the big bully's face, "Max isn't a prisoner, you hear, he's a dog! And we're not keeping any concentration camp on these premises!"

"You cuckoo," Dragomir observed dryly, "She now always wills do inside."

"So? It's me got to clean up after her, not you!"

And ever since then Max has been lolling in our armchairs quite legally again, and been followed about by the wife rag-in-hand. And she eats soup and chocolate, and we pootshie-mootshie her all de time, and she disembowels all over the place, and no garden, no chain, no nothing.

Dog Days

Then came the day when Max suddenly began showing an unnatural interest in dogs. From time to time she would jump up on the window-sill wagging her tail frantically and sounding short barks of *double entendre*. I would look out and lo and behold, all the dogs of the neighbourhood had assembled, and they were looking *in*. Zulu, the black shepherd who lives down the street, actually invaded our porch and tried to force the shutters.

Dragomir the dragon solved the mystery for us: "What for you so excites?" he said to my wife. "De bitch is heated."

"What?" the wife asked. "What do you mean, heated?"

"Love-love," Dragomir informed her. "She wants couplet."

He meant "copulate" of course. It seems that the summer heat brings on another kind of heat as well, and Max was heeding Nature's signals, to put it mildly. Even the children realized that our dog was going through a crisis.

"Dad," Amir asked me, "why is Max dying to go out to those dogs?"

"Son," Dad answered, "they want to play with her."

"Really?" Amir said, "I thought they wanted to have intercourse."

Actually he used a shorter word, but I'd hate to repeat it, even with the facts of life right on my doorstep, so to say. Before long the admirers in front of our house got so numerous that it was impossible to go out unless armed with a broom. The dogs were vaulting the garden fence and milling below Max's window. We fought the lovelorn hordes, shot jets of

165

water at them and stretched barbed wire across the garden gate, which the lovers chewed up in a matter of minutes. Once I even tossed rocks at Zulu, and he tossed them right back. And Max, that lost soul, draped herself about the window like a showcase dummy bursting with libido.

"Dad," said Amir, "how about letting her have a go?"

"No," I told him, "there are enough dogs in the world as it is."

"But she's dying to go out to them and . . ."

He used that word again.

"No," I answered stubbornly, "She ought to consider herself married. No extramarital larks, if you please."

But by now the passions were aflame. The dogs outside set up an all-male choir and started fighting among themselves, while Max cheered them on from the window. Things were getting out of hand. Our silly little darling neither ate nor slept, but only dreamt about her boy-friends all day. She was just aching for a chance to be fruitful and multiply.

My wife's opinion of her was short and to the point:

"Tart!"

Obviously the cause of all this erotic ferment was that Max was too beautiful. She was a real smasher, what with her soft liquid eyes and snow-white fur. We decided therefore to rescue the poor thing from the clutches of her own lust and reduce her sex appeal by shearing off her mane. We got in touch with the company providing this service, and next day two specialists came, beat a path through the all-male choir and took Max away for a haircut. Max fought like a mini-lioness, till at last, outnumbered and outwitted, she was dragged townwards accompanied by the protest barking of her myriad admirers, who raced the van as far as the outskirts of Tel Aviv.

We were left at home with our conscience.

"What else could I have done?" I sighed, rolling my eyes heavenwards, "She's still a minor, after all."

Our Max never returned from the hairdresser. Two completely exhausted specialists came back next day with an outsized pink mouse. So help me, I'd never have believed Max was so small inside. With her hair gone, she had turned into a fashion model whose most prominent features are her bones. Rafi suggested we rename her Twiggy. A cruel joke, I must say. She herself, our pink mouse, almost died with shame at her curtailed looks and wouldn't talk to us, only gazed out reproachfully through the cold window panes . . .

Then the unthinkable happened.

The iron gate of our garden of sin was torn off its hinges by the onrush of the new legions. Mad dogs were leaping at our window-panes day and night. If heretofore all the dogs of the neighbourhood had besieged our Max, now every single dog in the world was trying to get at her. I remember seeing a couple of Eskimo dogs who'd come straight from the North Pole to pootshie-mootshie it with Twiggy.

It turned out that hairless, Max was even more sexy. We had committed a fatal blunder: now she was stark naked. And exposed in a shop window. We had turned our house into a pornshop.

When one of the admirers, a bulldozer son-of-a-bitch, tore off the door handle with one blow, we quickly called the police before the dogs could cut the telephone lines. We meant to ask them to come and arrest the rowdies, but the line was busy. The ring of besiegers drew ever closer, for the sex problem is an acute one. Rafi proposed we set the bushes in the garden on fire and retreat with Twiggy to the nearest post office branch under cover of the flames, the way they do in the Tarzan movies when the aborigines attack. Meanwhile, however, Zulu had jumped down from the roof and burst into the kitchen, a clear threat in his eyes: "First I'll rape Twiggy, then I'll finish off Spectacles."

I engaged him in desperate duel, with my family's honour at stake, while Max ran in circles round us, obviously rooting for Zulu. The wild barking reached a new climax. My little family dug in behind the upturned furniture while outside the dogs rushed about, firing in our direction . . .

"Come," the woman panted, her face a deadly white, "give

them Max . . ."

"Never," I panted back. "I'll never surrender to blackmail!"

And then — the pen still trembles in my hand as I write — just when our ammunition had run out and everything seemed lost, the barking stopped outside and the platoons of dogs were gone as suddenly as they had appeared. Cautiously I put my head out and strained my ears for the trumpets of the relieving cavalry, which as a rule arrives at the last moment to save the settlers from the scalping knife, but there was no trace of an organized rescue. It must have been an ordinary miracle or something.

Next day Dragomir told us what had happened:

"I knows," he said, "at noon de heat brokes all over town. Finish!"

By now everything has returned to drab commonplace. Twiggy-mouse has reverted to a snow-white doggie interested only in men. She doesn't waste a glance on the neighbourhood dogs, and they reciprocate. The other day I saw that miserable Zulu passing her in the street: he ignored her completely. Max just didn't exist for him. Yet it seems that he is the sire of the little schnauzers we are expecting out of wedlock, to judge by all the physiological signs.

The Great Steak Saga

This tale would never have been written if Martin and Zion didn't serve you those steaks that look like a personal challenge to the Government's economic policy. The thing is that on Saturday we usually go for lunch to Martin and Zion's, and they put five huge steaks in front of us like so many Great God Browns. The first time it happened we thought there must be some mistake, they'd given us double portions, but it turned out this was only Martin-and-Zionist professional largesse, and not megalomania or anything. It's particularly tough on the kids, who after a while just sit and stare wanly at those Brobdingnagian portions on their plates:

"Mummy," wails Renana, "I can't eat any more . . ."

We grownups are frustrated too, even though — or rather, just because — M&Z's steaks are simply out of this world. It breaks your heart just to leave the better half of them on your plate. I wasn't surprised, therefore, when one Saturday just as our jaws were ready to drop off the little woman whispered to me:

"Why don't we take the rest home for supper?"

Quite. The question was: how? I mean, you can't simply get up and walk out of a restaurant with bits of steak dangling between finger and thumb, can you? Personally I still remember half a hamburger I once wrapped in a paper-napkin, stuck absently into my back-pocket and forgot all about, and on the way home when I wanted to take out my wallet in some shop, I stood there in the full glare of daylight with a handful of oozing, sticky, messy — don't remind me . . .

No, I decided, no illegal contraband for me this time. I

called Zion over:

"Would you mind wrapping up what's left of those steaks for the dog?"

You'll admit it was a bright idea to shift the blame onto Max. Zion returned from the kitchen with an enormous plastic bag and a benevolent smile:

"I added," he said, "some bones as well."

To be sure, there were at least 15 pounds of elephant-bones in that revolting bag, as well as a dozen raw kidneys and some liver complaint, all on top of the scraps and slops dredged up from the garbage pail. We thanked Zion nicely and at home we dumped the horror in front of Max and fled out of smelling range. Our fastidious bitch devoured the lot — except for the steaks.

A sadder and a wiser man, I decided next weekend upon a new strategy to gather ye steak bits:

"Please," I told Zion, "could you wrap the remains for our dog, but don't mix in any other meat."

It sounded like a plain enough order, but that fool Zion objected:

"Why?" he said, "We've got some delicious scraps for your doggie in the kitchen."

"It's very kind of you," thus I, "but our Max is a spoilt bitch. She'll touch nothing but steak."

At this point a hairy man sitting at a nearby table intervened:

"You're making a bad mistake, you know. You're feeding the poor animal on just about the worst kind of food you possibly could."

It turned out the guy was a veterinarian whom the gods had sent here expressly to torment us.

"Fried food is harmful to a canine's digestive system," our neighbour lectured the restaurant at large, "I wouldn't be surprised if that dog fails to grow on a diet like that. What breed is he?"

"A miniature schnauzer," I said rebelliously, "And he's a bitch."

With these words I turned my back on the vet and told

Zion to wrap up the steaks separately.

The vet shuddered and looked pained, but Zion disappeared into the kitchen, and returned in a minute with our steaks all done up nicely in a newspaper.

"What's the matter with you?" I yelled at him, "You run out of bags or what?"

"Dunno," said Zion all innocence, "Why?"

Why indeed! How explain to that wretch that I can't bring myself to eat steaks which have been wrapped up in last week's strikes and kidnappings. We flung the muck out of the window on our way home.

We refused to give up the dog-fight, however, and the following Saturday we were back at M&Z's armed with a shining new plastic bag. The hairy vet sat nearby and looked on in speechless rage as Zion handed us our home-delivery in a nice hygienic parcel at last. Our steak-feast lasted for three whole days. It seems steak matures with age, like vintage wine. We had steak for supper that night, steak for breakfast next morning, and for several mornings after. Max lay on her belly and pensively watched us stuffing ourselves, but refused to touch any herself . . .

The crisis came a month later when, like all good things, our honeymoon with steak came to an end. The daily grind was beginning to wear us down:

"Ephraim," declared the woman one day in February, "I've had enough."

So had we all. Next Saturday we ordered schnitzel, and what's more, we ordered it from Martin. And after lunch our kind-hearted Zion, that idiot, came up to us toting a bagful of secondhand steaks.

"For Max!" he announced, the crazy dog-lover.

Each Saturday after that we would leave Martin and Zion's wondering how to get rid of our *embarras de steakesse*. I mean, you can't just drive about town leaving trails of meat behind you. Before you know it, the literary supplements will come out with gleeful headlines: "WRITER OR BUTCHER?"

We were all gradually turning into fanatical anti-Zionists.

171

Then, on the first Saturday in March, we had a brainwave:

"Zion," we informed the dear fellow sadly, "No more steaks. Max is dead."

We lowered our eyes as Zion pressed our hand in mute sympathy. At the other end of the restaurant the vet stood up hairily and screamed:

"See! I warned you! You killed the dumb brute yourself!"

We hung our heads in shame. Rafi muttered something about poor Max having been run over by a car, but that only added fuel to the burning vet. We slunk out of there with our tail between our legs, albeit steakless, and drove home feeling like a bunch of killers. If now we should find our little Max dead on the doorstep, we told ourselves, it'd be no more than we deserved. The cheerful barks that greeted us on arrival put our conscience at rest. Max was saved!

For some time after that we lived a simple happy life, uncomplicated by long-play steaks and such. Till yesterday in fact, when the little woman turned to me and said in a neutral sort of voice:

"Are we going to Zion's on Saturday?"

I looked at her and saw that the steak-bug had got her again, though what we're going to do now that we've killed off Max I can't think. If worst comes to worst we may have to invent a new puppy for that fool Zion, considering what's at steak.

A Straight Flush

We had asked the Lustigs over for tea and they had brought their six-year-old Moishele along, though we hadn't asked *him*. We aren't all that keen on visitors who bring their offspring with them, though I admit Moishele was as good as gold and only wandered through the house looking at things. We adults discussed nuclear warfare and the end of the world generally, which was a bore. Then we heard Moishele flush the toilet.

No great event, you'd say, but the Lustigs jumped and looked all anxious.

"Moishele!" they cried, "What was that?"

"The key of Mr. Kishon's wardrobe," he answered calmly, giving us his sweetest smile. The Lustigs picked up their son, planted him on the sofa with a reprimand and a picture-book, then turned back to us.

"It hurts us to talk about it," Mr. Lustig unburdened himself, "Moishele is a perfectly normal child, except he has this thing about keys. He sees a key, he simply *must* flush it down there. It's only keys — nothing else. We don't know *what* to do about it. People have told us we ought to simply ignore it, act like we didn't care, and eventually the kid would give it up on his own account. We tried that, but the only result was we ended up without a key in the house."

"Tell me, Moishele," I asked the tot, "Why do you flush down keys?"

"Dunno," Moishele answered dreamily, "It's fun."

"We even took him to see a psychiatrist," Mrs. Lustig said gloomily, "He fired questions at Moishele for two hours, and in the end he asked us had we ever hit the child with a key when he was little. I told him keys were too small for that, so we argued about it for a while till we suddenly heard a flush of water. We had to phone a locksmith — Moishele had locked us in. The psychiatrist had a nervous fit . . ."

Just then we heard the familiar sound again. This time it was the front-door key.

"You don't live high up, do you?" the wretched parents asked.

"No," I said, "A yard or two."

They jumped out through the window and promised to send us a locksmith. I was left to myself and my thoughts. After a while I suddenly got up, took the key of my room and flushed it down the toilet. So help me, there's something to be said for it.

Actor-Mans on Strings

It all started with Doron, who announced at nursery school one day: "Me I seen Piccoli". One bystander, an infant young in years but wonderfully bright for her age and strikingly handsome, ran to her father and said:

"Daddy, I want Piccoli."

"You're too young to go to the theatre," replied her father firmly, "I don't want to hear another word on the subject, and that's final!"

The time has come to reveal that the above speakers are, respectively, this writer and his youngest daughter Renana, and it follows that they went to the puppet-show all right.

On the way there I learnt that my daughter's acquaintance with matters theatrical was surprisingly vast. She seemed to have a natural flair for the stage, as indeed she told me herself:

"When I'm big I'll play in the theatre."

"What'll you play?"

"Hopscotch."

It may have been owing to just such gaps in her knowledge that when the lights went out my little girl panicked:

"Daddy," she breathed, "Why's it all dark?"

"It's always dark in the theatre."

"Why?"

"Because that's how it is."

"But why?"

We carry on this kind of meaningful conversation all the time. Once you're stuck on the why-track with her you'll never get unstuck again, except by introducing startling new elements into the situation, like: "Look, sweetie, Daddy's standing on his head!" or "Bubble gum, anyone?"

Bringing up children isn't as easy as it sounds. Like how do you explain to such a slip of a girl that it has to be dark in the theatre because the visual-focal impact . . . the concentration . . . dunno . . .

"Renana!" I said crossly, "Be quiet now or we'll go home!" Here, fortunately, the curtain went up and the stage filled with cute little marionettes who started romping about. Renana watched them with great goggle-eyes:

"Daddy, why are those silly thingummies dancing?"

"They're dancing because they're so glad Renana is here."

"Go away, thingummies!" cried Renana, "Stop it!"

"Shhh! Don't shout!"

"Then why're they dancing?"

"It's their profession. Like Daddy writes, Renana wrecks the house — actors dance."

At this point Renana began to sing, "Lousy in the ska-hy with da-hy-mous", and some members of the audience around us grew restless. A few even produced unsubtle remarks about idiot parents taking their idiot babies to the theatre. I saw that Renana was about to burst into tears at this hostile reception, so I said quickly:

"Look, darling! See how high that puppet can jump?"

"Not puppet!" Renana corrected me, "Actor man!"

"It isn't a man, sweetie, it's just a puppet."

"No!" said Renana, "Man!"

"Don't you see it's made of wood?"

"Wood? Like trees?"

"No! Like tables!"

I never cared much for Doron myself. The silence at my side lasted for a full minute. I was getting worried.

"Daddy," said Renana at last, "Why strings?"

"Puppets are pulled on strings."

"Not puppets! Mans!"

I realized I'd never be able to cope with this on my own, so I called on an usher for help:

"Please, mister, are those actors, or just puppets?"

"Course they're not puppets," said that ass with a huge wink at me, "Those are real actors!"

Renana sent me a pitying glance. She never thought much of my intellect. Puppets singing and dancing! What next?

"Daddy," she said, "Why haven't I got strings on me?"

"Because you aren't a puppet."

"I am too! Mummy says I am!"

There, now she was crying. "You're a puppet, you're a puppet," I assured her. The little animals which appeared on the stage next saved the day:

"Bow-wow!" began Renana, surveying them, "Miaow! Moo! Cock-a-doodle-doo! Daddy, what's that?"

She was pointing at something that looked like a cross between a chipmunk and an ox.

"Oo," I said, "Isn't it pretty?"

"But what *is* it?"

"A gnu," I said in despair.

"Why?"

I left that theatre a sadder and a thinner man, Renana in my arms still full of pep:

"My daddy says," she explained to the crowd, "that the actor-mans are tied up with string so's they shan't run away."

Her dispassionate audience seemed to care little how one daddy had reached this conclusion, and only eyed me contemptuously as much as to say: some parents cram their children full of the weirdest nonsense, and the police stand by and do nothing.

"Daddy," said Renana by way of summing up, "I *don't* want to play in the theatre."

If that's the Piccoli's sole achievement, then their visit to this country has not been in vain.

Zoo Story

My publisher is a pleasant sort of fellow who has the welfare of his writers at heart. One day, therefore, he took me aside and said:

"Look, you better think twice before you start on your next, because the latest surveys show nobody reads books any more."

"Come, come," I said, "I personally know a couple who buy at least two books a year."

"That's as may be," said my publisher, "But I can't put out a whole edition for just one couple. Anyway, I've been thinking. Why don't you write a children's book? Children still do read."

"Sure," I said, "Why not? A children's book. What's selling now?"

"Animals."

"Very well, I'll write you an animal story."

"What animal?"

"Um . . . a billy-goat. Kiddie the Bill. How's that?"

"Ha" – thus my publisher – "Been done before: 'Gilly the Goat'. Sold eight printings. Not a bad story either. Gilly runs away from home in a jeep, but after many adventures he finds that home is best after all and goes back to mama goat. You'll have to come up with something a bit less common . . ."

"Like what? A bear maybe?"

"I just published the last of our 'Bobby the Bugbear' series last week Bobby runs away from home because he's got this bug about wide open spaces, but in the end he returns home

178

because he finds that home is the best place after all. We've had everything, chum — dogs, cats, cows, camels, mice, lice, the lot . . ."

"How about a zebra?"

"Got one. 'Eebra the Zebra Joins the IRA'. Sixteen printings."

"Does he run away from home?"

"Yes, in a jeep. You'll have to find something new."

"A lemming."

"Don't be funny, it's been at the top of the best-seller list for a month: 'Lemming Go, Lemming Go!' It runs away . . ."

"A bat?"

" 'Alladin the Bat and the 40 Thieves'. This silly little bat leaves home . . ."

"In a jeep?"

"No, he *returns* in a jeep."

My publisher fetched the catalogue.

"Hardly an unemployed animal left," he mumbled, as he ran his finger down the list, "There — 'Iggy the Eagle at the Olympic Games', 'Cuckoo the Merry Marmot', 'Hutch the Hippo' who runs away to become a hippie . . ."

"Got it!" I shouted, "A woodworm!"

"Twenty-three printings," my publisher snorted, " 'Joseph the Woodworm Goes Fishing'. Fairly amusing. He gets to America on this ship . . ."

"How?"

"Hides in a cargo of jeeps."

"I see. Well, I suppose there's nothing left me then but a flea."

" 'Lea the Flea Fixes the Cops'. Came out this autumn. She runs away from home, goes to the flea-market, not a bad story at all . . ."

"Snakes. Got any snakes?"

"Crawling with them. 'Creepy the Viper at the Travelling Circus'. He gets friendly with the boy next door, and they run away with Betsy the Beetle . . ."

"Codfish?"

" 'Shimmele the Codfish Hijacks a Plane'."

"Snails?"

" 'Micky and Moocky the Snooty Snails'. They're twins and they run away from the home on their backs, but they return because it's cold outside."

"Very well," I sighed, "A sea sponge."

"Splendid!" — he beamed at me — "I don't believe that's been done yet. You'll have to write fast, though, because once the word gets round there'll be three different versions in the bookshops before you can say scat . . ."

"Leave it to me," thus I, "You can add it to your catalogue: 'Spooner the Sponge Goes to Town'."

"Shoot!"

I drove home hell for leather, and in two days I'd finished the first in the series. It turned out quite well too: Spooner runs away from home to become a bath-sponge in Jerusalem, but after all sorts of adventures he returns home. I think he'd better return in a jeep. Play it safe.

Gone with the Window

One night we were sitting snugly at home with a pile of magazines when the doorbell rang. The little woman looked at me, then back at her mag, so I got up to see who it was. It was a pleasant-looking couple in their mid-forties and slippers. They introduced themselves as Dov and Lucy Gross from across the street, apologized for the late hour, and asked could they come in for a moment.

I opened the door wider to let them in, and they headed straight for the living room, walked round the piano, and stopped in front of the tea trolley.

"There!" Lucy cried triumphantly to her husband, "*Not* a sewing machine!"

"All right," Dov snapped back, "All right, you win. But I was right last time: they don't have the 'Britannica'."

"You bastard," Lucy turned on him, "I never said 'Britannica' — just that they had *an* encyclopaedia, and that they looked like snobs."

"Like hell you did! I should have taken you down on tape, that's all."

"Too bad you didn't."

I thought I'd better intervene before they came to blows, and suggested we all sit down and talk it over calmly like grownup people. Dov took off his raincoat and remained in blue cotton pyjamas with stripes.

"We live right opposite you," he explained, pointing at the high-rise across the street, "There, see? Second floor. Well, we've got these fantastic binoculars — got them in Hong

Kong last year."

"Uh-huh," said I, "The Japanese are very good at that sort of thing."

"This one's got like one to twenty magnification," Lucy announced, adjusting a stray roller in her hair, "We can see everything down to the last detail in your place with them. So yesterday Dov kept insisting that this dark shape behind your piano was a sewing machine, and I was ready to bet it wasn't, or you wouldn't put a flower vase on top. So in the end I said to him: Know what, I said, let's go over there and see who's right."

"Absolutely," I nodded, "The only way to settle this kind of argument. And was that all?"

"No," sighed Dov, "There's those curtains too, those flowered curtains you have on your bedroom windows. When you draw them we can't see."

"I'm sorry," I said, "We only draw them to keep the sun out in the morning . . ."

"Look, I'm not blaming you," thus Dov, "I mean, you don't have to consider us. It's your house, after all."

Rapport had definitely been established. The little woman came in with tea and biscuits.

"I wonder if that chewing-gum's still there," said Dov, ducking under the table and probing the underside with his fingers. "Pink chewing-gum it was."

"Yellow!"

"Pink!"

They were at it again. Really, a nice, civilized couple like that — and yet they couldn't talk for five minutes without starting a row. The chewing-gum, it turned out, was green. So they weren't infallible after all.

"That man who came to see you last night," Dov explained, "he put it there. Tall, distinguished sort of fellow — but when you left the room for a minute he took it out of his mouth and stuck it under the table."

"What fun," the little one giggled, "You really do see everything."

"We haven't got TV," Dov explained, "So we've nothing to look at all evening. You don't mind, do you?"

"No, why should we?"

The little one brought fruit and icecream.

"Keep an eye on that window-cleaner of yours," Dov advised us, "He's been using your aftershave."

"You mean you can see into our bathroom?"

"Not all of it. Just the towel-rack and part of the shower."

They also warned us against our new babysitter:

"She pops the kids into bed," said Lucy, "and ten minutes later she's in bed herself with the boyfriend."

"Tsk, tsk," I said, "is your view of our bedroom that good?"

"Yeah, except for those curtains, as I said."

"But the sun . . ."

"I know, I know," said Dov with a trace of impatience in his voice. "But it *is* a nuisance, if you don't mind my saying so."

"Dov!" said Lucy, "Mind your manners!"

"Yeah," said Dov, getting up, "Well, it was nice meeting you in the flesh. You're a bit fatter than I thought, though," he added, turning to me, "You've got a proper pot-belly there, you know? I'd recommend a diet."

"Thanks."

"Not at all. We're neighbours, after all."

We promised to keep in touch, and they left. A minute later the light came on at their place, then Dov's figure appeared in the window and he raised his binoculars. We waved at him, and he gestured in a sort of don't-mind-me, carry-on-as-usual way.

"Charming people," said the wife, "So delightfully informal."

"Yes," said I, "Quite like old friends already. I feel as if they'd known us for years."

The Apollo Mission

"Ephraim," said the little woman, "Amir's in a mood." Preparations for the Purim Carnival were in full swing. Rafi was duly fixed up as a pirate with a slight touch of Military Police, Renana was Queen Esther, but Amir was sulking about the house with a face like thunder. Now and then he would aim a passing kick at the splendid costume that his mummy had made for him with her own hands. The fringed pants, the rubber boots, the ten-gallon hat, the gilded belt, and last but not least the stinking pistol — a complete outfit for the perfect cowboy — lay in a dark corner in utter *non grata,* while the *persona* himself was getting moodier by the moment.

"What's the matter, Amir?" we enquired at last. "Don't you want to be a cowboy?"

"No," said Amir, "I want to be an astronaut."

He'd just been reading about Apollo 13 in his children's weekly.

"Pipe down," we told our son, "and we'll see what can be done."

"That's right," agreed the little woman, "we must talk it over and decide."

We held an impromptu parents meeting and agreed the kid had a point: who *wouldn't* want to be an astronaut, mankind's spinning conscience? Gradually a compromise was hammered out: "You be a cowboy just this time," we suggested to Amir, "and next year you can be an astronaut."

"No!" yelled our temperamental offspring, "I want it now!"

I suppose the legal term is: a Case of Irresistible Impulse.

"All right," we gave in with heavy heart, "so be an astronaut. We'll put a big pan on top of your head, and we'll write on it in red paint: 'Apollo 13' . . ."

"That's silly!" shrieks Amir fortissimo, "that's not an astronaut!"

"Then what is?"

"I don't know," sobs the child, *"you* ought to know!"

Why don't those guys fly to the moon *after* Purim? Is it too much to expect the U.S. Government to show some consideration for Israeli parents? Just listen to the kid's screams:

"Astro" – he screams – "nau-hau-haut!"

"All right," I say, "we'll stick a big moustache on your face."

"Don't want silly moustache! Astronautses don't have moustaches."

"A pair of glasses then!"

"Astronautses don't . . ."

Damn thoughtless of them, I must say! How on earth can a responsible person fly to the moon without a moustache, without glasses, without any recognizable mark of identification whatsoever?

"Got it!" I say. "Amir shall put on Daddy's yellow pyjamas . . ."

"Don't want silly pyjamas," howls the kid, "Wanna be a proper astronaut!"

"Let Daddy finish, will you? You'll wear my yellow pyjamas and we'll stick a propeller in your botty. A real propeller than turns."

"Don't want silly propeller!"

"Wings then . . ."

"Not a silly bird! An astronaut!"

All that running about in space is nothing but a silly adventure, if you ask me.

"Dad-dy! As-tro!"

The child nearly has a fit on the carpet. Only redheads can cry like that, back and forth and sideways with never a breath

185

in between. Got to save him before he blows his little lungs:

"No problem at all," says Daddy, "let's ring up Uncle Astronaut and ask him."

Amir falls incredibly silent, his blue eyes wide with hope. I pick up the phone and dial at random:

"Hallo, Apollo Headquarters?" I address the receiver. "Could I talk to the duty astronaut, please?"

"Who you wanting?" asks a woman at the other end of the line, "This Dr. Weisberger house."

"Hi Winston!" I exclaim joyfully, "How're things? Look, Amir wants to know how you're got up for your trip to the moon."

"Who?" — that woman again — "This Dr. Weisberger house."

"Hold on, Winston, I'll get a pencil," thus Daddy, "Now then, what do you say you're wearing? Fringed pants, rubber boots, ten-gallon hat . . ."

"I not knowing Hebrew so good. Speak you German please?"

"Sure, I'm writing it down, Winston. Gilded belt and pistol. Fine, that's all I wanted to know. Give my regards to the President."

"Dr. Weisberger coming home in twelve."

"Thanks a lot."

I replace the receiver with a worried frown:

"Heard that?" I turn to Mummy. "Now where the hell are we going to get Amir all these things that astronauts wear?"

"Nuts!" shouts the idiot child dizzy with triumph. "They're there in the corner! . . ."

That's how disaster was averted at the last moment with the aid of telecommunication. And if, dear reader, you should happen to see a very small cowboy with red hair about town these days, please cry out at the top of your voice: "Oho, there goes a real astronaut!" By the way, it's time they put a stop to those moon flights. They cost the earth.

Merry-Go-Round

It is more blessed to give than to receive, as the saying goes, and it follows that whenever we come across some useless object at home, we say to ourselves: Good, that'll do fine as a present for somebody. What's more, we keep a regular supply of gifts on hand, all neatly filed and indexed and ready for use. Whenever someone brings us a present, we say thank you nicely and store it away under its proper heading. Baby things, for instance, go straight to the Brith-Milah department, Hebrew classics — to the Barmitzvah reserve, horrid knickknacks — to Weddings, cheap flowerpots — to Birthdays, ashtrays — House-warmings, etcetera — etcetera.

However.

One dark day Ben-Zion Ziegler showed up with one of those fancy boxes of chocolates, complete with smirking beauty and pink roses on the lid. We were very happy with it, since a chocolate-box is a particularly useful gift, good for all seasons. We were just about to add it to the Miscellaneous Junk Department, when something really shattering happened: all of a sudden we felt like a chocolate. We tore off the cellophane with eager hands, opened the box — and discovered some dozen rocks green with mildew inside . . .

"That beats everything," said the little woman, "To give us antique chocolate . . ."

We stormed out of the house and went to see Ziegler. He looked, blushed, and explained with a sheepish grin that actually he'd received this chocolate himself last year from his good friend Bar-Honig, for having got his M.S.E. at last. We rang up Bar-Honig and asked what the hell. The fellow hemmed and hawed a bit, then confessed he'd got the box from Glick in honour of the Six-Day-War victory. Onward. Glick had received it four years before when his wife had the twins, from his cousin (the chocolate, not the twins). The cousin had got it from Goldstein (1963), who sent us on to Kruyf, Kruyf to Pele, Pele to Aunt Ilka, Aunt Ilka to . . . yes . . . to us. Sure, I remembered, we'd given it to her that time she was in hospital with a broken leg . . . 1961 that was . . .

So this chocolate had gone up and down the whole country, had been at every feast, birthday and hen-party in the land — and now it had perished at our hands. Maybe if we hadn't opened it, this box might have lived another 50 years or so before it crumbled.

We, at any rate, feel it's our duty to inform the public at large that this country's only chocolate-box has been withdrawn from circulation. Someone will have to buy a new one and set the wheel spinning again. Sorry.

Telecomplications

An Israeli citizen travelling abroad feels badly out of touch with the homeland. Once in a while he may see a map of Sinai flashing for a second on the telly, receive a hand-me-down Israeli magazine, or a letter from home to say they'll write more next time. That's all. Of course there's always the telephone still. Very handy, very useful instrument, nothing like it for establishing immediate contact with a man's family, have them right there — close, intimate, infinitely dear. Dear is right: a call from somewhere like New York City costs a man eight solid dollars for every minute of conversation.

Ah, what the hell!

The Israeli-abroad takes a deep breath, picks up the receiver in his bare little hotel-room and dials 009723 with steady finger. Beep-beep-beep, goes the tried and true instrument, beep-beep-beep. I'll just discuss the really burning issues with my wife — I prime myself — or this phone-call will eat up my whole foreign currency allowance. Everything all right at home? Kids okay? Good. I'm fine, dear, yes I'll get home soon's I can. don't pay the property-tax yet, there's time, kiss-kiss, that's it. Three minutes at most, short and sweet . . .

Oops!

"Hallo," a small familiar voice pipes up on the other side of the ocean, "Whosit?"

It's my little girl Renana. A warm glow fills my heart.

"Hallo, sweetie!" I yell into the receiver, "How are you?"

"Whosit?" says Renana, "Hallo."

"This is Daddy!"

"What?"

"Daddy, this is Daddy here! Is Mummy home?"

"Who's that there?"

"Daddy!"

"My Daddy?"

"Yes, this is your Daddy here! Get Mummy, darling!"

"Waidaminute . . . Daddy, listen Daddy . . ."

"Yes!"

"How are you?"

"Fine, just fine, where's Mummy?"

"You're in America now, you're in America, right?"

"Yes, got to hurry though . . ."

"Do you want to talk to Amir?"

I can't say no or I'll hurt his feelings.

"All right, but hurry! So long, sweetie!"

"What?"

"So long, I said!"

"Whosit?"

"Put Amir on!"

"So long, Daddy!"

"So long, sweetie, so long!"

"What?"

"Put Amir on, dammit!"

"Amir, where are you? Daddy wants you, Amir! Amee-ee-eer! . . ."

That's seven fat minutes gone. They shouldn't allow children near these instruments. Where's that idiot boy? Amee-ee-eer!

"Hallo, Daddy?"

"Yes, my boy, how are you?"

"Fine, how are you?"

"Fine. Everything all right, Amir?"

"Yes."

"Splendid."

A brief silence. We've gone over everything, I believe.

"Daddy!"

"Yes."

"Renana wants to talk to you."

I picture a sort of taxi-meter, only bigger, and with alarming figures running amok inside — click — IL.360 — click — IL.396 — click — IL.432 — click . . .

"Daddy, listen Daddy . . ."

"Yes!"

"Yesterday . . . yesterday . . ."

"Yesterday what?"

"Yesterday . . . waidaminute! Amir, *let* me talk to Daddy! Daddy, Amir's *pushing* me."

"Get Mummy quick!"

"What?"

"I want Mummy!"

"Waidaminute . . . Yesterday . . ."

"Yes!"

"Yesterday . . . yesterday . . . you hear me?"

"Yes, I hear you, yesterday, what happened yesterday, what happened, yesterday, what happened?"

"Yesterday Moshik didn't come to kindergarten."

"Where's Mummy?"

"What?"

"M-u-m-m-y!"

"Mummy isn't home. Daddy, listen Daddy . . ."

"Yeah, what?"

"Do you want to talk to Amir?"

"No, never mind! Bye-bye, sweetie!"

"Who?"

"K-i-s-s!"

"Yesterday . . ."

At this point the connection is suddenly broken. Maybe I touched the cradle or something. My eyes are glazed, my heart bleeds, my blood curdles. The blasted instrument tinkles merrily — the operator's well-bred voice: "That'll be 166 dollars and 70 cents, Mr. Kitchen."

End-of-Year Entertainment

"You *will* come, Daddy, won't you?"

"Yes, I will."

This brief dialogue between myself and my middle son Amir had been repeating itself twice a day for the past six months — once before breakfast and once at bedtime. His teacher Nediva, that is, had given the child a leading part in the end-of-year performance, and from that moment on he had spent the time in his room, standing in a circle and reciting the authorized text like a stuck record.

"Little rabbit grab it Babbit," his voice would ring out beyond the wall, "moon soon tree glee pink clink . . ." and more of the unpunctuated same. He'd even walk to school mumbling bits of rosy-posy-busy-bee and this-went-to-market or something.

When the time came, the classroom itself was bursting at the seams with pictures of Israeli scenery, and I could barely squeeze myself in between the Sea of Galilee and the cakes. The room was hot, and the abundance of fond parents boded ill. In such a situation an average daddy like myself has the choice between two I-won't-say-evils: he can either sit on a chair and see the backs of necks, or stand up and see his son. I chose the compromise of sitting on the back of a chair, behind a mum with a back-to-front baby who kept staring at me bleakly and sniffing me with nervous suspicion. "Daddy," my son asked before we parted, "you *staying*?"

"Yes, I'm staying."

Amir found a place on the limelit bench and the

communal singing started with communal gusto: *Anu banu, Hinei ma tov, Hava nagi-hi-hi-la.* We parents joined in whenever teacher was looking. Then a freckled boy stepped forward to address the parents:

"To Jerusalem let us go, Land-of-Israel-we-love-you-so, They fought and knew no fear, Parents, parents dear . . ."

Remember, I'm sitting at some distance from the scene of action and the text reaches my ears a bit droopily. Just now, for instance, a miniscule youth is reciting something about the Land of Israel, and I hear nothing but receive only visual impressions. My son keeps checking up on me, and so does the back-to-front baby. Riotous applause, and I ask is this the end?

"The class flute orchestra," replies the little compere on stage. "Landler of our land!"

I am extremely fond of the flute as such, but out in the country, not among dense urban crowds. Grade Four counts four musicians among its members, so we are going to have four numbers in order to let them have a solo apiece: one Nardi, one Haydn, one Schoenberg and one Dvorak — the Land of Israel Suite. The windows are getting crowded with newspaper-reading daddies. Quite openly too, which isn't nice. I borrow somebody's sports page. When the concert ends we applaud very carefully, but not carefully enough.. Encore: Beethoven's "Leonora". If that damn baby doesn't take his damn eyes off me I don't know what I'll do . . .

Hey!

My son rises and moves towards the stage. With a chair. Seems that for the moment he's only acting as stage hand. "You there?" his eyes ask. "I'm here," I answer with a tiny twitch of my ear. My own son, after all. Why don't they hold these parties outside, in the fields and meadows? Or at the pool? A delightful tot has climbed up on my son's prop and proclaims himself to be Shlemer the Dreamer.

I decide to listen to this, come what may, and rivet my attention on Shlemer's lips.

"So you wonder why, so I'll tell you, fellas" — thus

Shlemer — "My mum said what so I went and yelled fellas it's a cat so the cat too and then whadyethink? Believe it or not fellas he went oops and suddenly grabbed him so whadyethinkfellas? He was all over chalk!"

The children burst out laughing, I must be going gaga. I concentrate, I'm an antenna, all of me, and yet I can't catch a single sentence whole. I notice that the other daddies are breathing hard as well. By the door, Shlemer's mummy and teacher Nediva are haggling: the mummy points out what a lot of hard work has gone into preparing the act, and Nediva says one more joke and that's it.

Mummy: Three. Compromise: Three, with a little Land of Israel thrown in, fellas, he spoke and sang and so he couldn't find and bang.

One hour gone. The mum with the back-to-fronter collapses noisily into the cakes. I rush over to help her out into the fresh air, but a few seasoned daddies forestall me and joyfully sweep her out. What do they mean, the party's not over yet, is it?

"And now," says the compere, "the Cock-a-doodle-doo Swingers in Birds of Eretz Israel!"

I'm not really all that fond of children. That is, I'm very fond of them, but in small quantities and not all of them together like that. They're lousy actors too. Just look at them now, jumping about like puppets to the sound of the flute quartet and singing: Naughty Cock-a-doodle-doo, tum-tum-tum flowers too, little chirper carrot, something something parrot . . .

I'm worn out. The windows are obscured by parents gasping for air, kid sisters want pee-pee, their daddies are smoking in the yard in open revolt. My son waves to me:

Don't budge, I'm on soon. I drag myself as far as Nediva and ask will we have an intermission? Impossible, she says, the party'll take too long.

"It's not so short as it is," I hint subtly.

"Every child must have a leading part," Nediva apologizes, "otherwise there's jealousy."

A few enviable daddies whose offspring have already done their numbers are gone with the wind. The beginnings of a Biblical spectacle in five acts are sorting themselves out on stage. My son is dispensing props again, damn him. This time I manage to get a peep at the script, which Nicky's brother holds in a shaking hand to prompt as needed.

Egyptian taskmaster (raising a whip): Labour with rigour, ye idlers!

Child of Israel: We have toiled since dawn and are weary. Hast thou no compassion?

I know heaps of people who never married and begot, and they're happy as larks. Besides, one more peep out of a Hebrew flute and I'll lose control.

Oops!

All of a sudden things take a drastic turn. The whole party gets into shape, fills with interest, a certain *je ne sais quoi* that makes one sit up and take notice. A handsome child comes on stage – my son, I presume. He's Mendele Mocher Seforim or something, it's hard to tell offhand.

"Moon soon tree glee pink clink ooga nahooga . . ." My little redhead reels off his leading part loud and clear. With modest pride I look round at the audience and get a shock: absolute indifference on every face and in every glassy eye. And that when Amir's every word is audible! His acting is medium-to-good, his diction reasonable, but his voice is clear all right. Never was such a clear voice heard in the Land of Israel. He's positively screaming – and they nod!

"*Ahat-shtayim,*" declaims my Mendele, "*lehayim, Givatayim, raglayim . . .*"

Every line rhymes with *Yerushalayim,* see? Come to think of it, I'm called *Ephrayim* myself. Clever. I applaud my redhead wildly. He waves: "Daddy, you – you?" Yes, it is I, my son, bless you!

Amir has come to the end of his number and sits down in good order. It's getting dark outside. Nediva is nudging the compere.

"What?" I ask her, amazed, "still more?"

"What do you mean, *more?*" she replies. "We're starting on our Beautiful Land of Israel Pageant, twelve tableaux with commentary . . ."

The cast don sheets and paper hats. Flutes. Commentary. Male choir. *Hora hagalila hagalil.* Drums. *Yerushalayim.* "In the beginning God all of a sudden created the heavens and let there be a land . . ." opens Nicky. The rest has slipped my mind.

Laundry Alarm

I woke at about one in the morning to the roar of a wounded lion. The sound was coming from outside and seemed to go on and on. I gave my sleeping wife's back a slight nudge:

"Hey!" I yelled into her ears, "You hear that?"

"Alarm," muttered the little woman with her eyes shut, "They're robbing the laundry . . ."

I agreed that was probably it, pulled the pillow over my ears and tried to go back to sleep, but my heart was going pit-a-pat on account of I thought perhaps we had washing there and who knows what'd happen to it. I nudged my wife again:

"What'll we do?"

"There's cotton-wool in the bathroom," hissed the wife, "You can get me some too . . ."

I looked through the window. A white convertible sedan stood in front of the laundry with its headlights full on. The alarm went like mad and was getting shriller by the second. I shut the window and saw other people on the block doing likewise. The noise was definitely unpleasant. We plugged up our ears, the little woman and I, and tried to sleep, but soon the phone at my bedside went:

"Please," said a hoarse voice, "I saw you at the window just now. The laundry, is it?"

"Yeah. Burglars."

"Again?"

It was the third or fourth time in this past half year. In

November they'd simply smashed the iron door with big hammers. It took them the best part of an hour and everybody on the block went right deaf with the noise of those crashing blows. They picked the place clean to the last pair of dirty socks.

Next day old Mr. Wertheimer ordered a special steel shutter for his laundry, and the burglars were obliged to saw through each separate link in turn. The job lasted till dawn and had us all in jitters, because there's nothing like a saw on metal to set your teeth on edge good. Really, you wonder how the robbers themselves stand it. Then, some two weeks back, old Wertheimer installed a terribly smart alarm system, all electronics and Dutch know-how. It's got those clever photo-cells, infra-red and all, which set an alarm bell going at the touch of a finger.

"Why the devil don't they cut the wires once they're inside?" grumbled my hoarse caller, "I'll write to the Mayor. I pays my taxes and I wants my sleep!"

"At the pharmacy," I said "they sell those wax things for your ears. Take two for alarm."

"Got them," said Hoarse, "No good."

"Oh," I said, "Well, then I don't know. Who's that speaking there?"

He hung up at once. Didn't want to be connected or something. I looked out. A couple of little men were mooching in front of the laundry, and one fellow was standing on another one's shoulders and measuring something with a tape. They still hadn't got in and the alarm rang fit to bust your eardrums. Those Dutch are real thorough when it comes to equipment like that. Philips and all.

"How about a sandwich?" I asked my wife, but she dozed on. She'd had a tough day with the kids. Somebody knocked at the door. My neighbour Felix Selig burst in looking cute in pink pyjamas and red eyes:

"What do you think?" I said, "You think this'll go on all night?"

When it comes to electricity Felix is a real whiz, like he

mends the fuses himself when they blow. He explained the situation to me: If this alarm works on batteries then all's well, seeing as how they're bound to run out in like five-six minutes. But if it's hooked up right into the grid . . .

"Last Purim they broke into a big furniture store in North Tel Aviv," Felix told me, "and three Japanese alarmsystems were going full blast for hours. People on that street thought they'd go nuts. Properly ruined their Purim for them. In the end the wires melted. Guys took the whole caboodle away on stolen trucks . . ."

They say there's this new plastic stuff you stick round your windows: seals them hermetic and keeps the draught out too. Felix promised he'd get me a sample from his kid brother, the one who married the daughter of that guy from the supermarket last January. The young couple're just back from the Far East. Had a fabulous trip, I hear.

Out in the street the alarm had been joined by a new noise, and flickers of light streaked our wall. The burglars had put a welding machine to the job. A few passers-by had collected and stood watching with their fingers in their ears . . .

I asked Felix how much he reckoned insurance'd pay in a case like this, and he said you could get 60 per cent out of them, but at least it was net. They say old Wertheimer wants to sell the laundry, it's getting too much for him. His son-in-law has been managing the place for him but now *he* wants to get back into real estate. I made us a halva sandwich each and we opened a tin of olives.

We saw Mrs. Shtuptzich from across open her window and shout something down, but we couldn't hear what on account of the noise. The driver of the white sedan got out and shouted back. Selig claimed he'd asked: "What're you called, lady?" Vulgar clod. Mrs. Shtuptzich got fed up and shut her window quick. All of a sudden we heard a whacking explosion and the sky over Tel Aviv went all white. A couple of minutes later the alarm fizzled out. They'd cut the wires at last. About time too.

"So come to bed," whispered the little woman, "It's

almost morning already . . ."

I had two-and-a-half hours' sleep left. I pulled the blanket over my head. Guess we'll have to switch laundries.

Peanuts

"Ephraim, are you sure it's for dinner?"

"I think I'm sure . . ."

We'd been into this before.

Mrs. Pomerantz had phoned to invite us for Wednesday evening at 8.30, I'd said fine, thank you, and we'd been analyzing that conversation ever since, because Mrs. Pomerantz hadn't said it was for dinner, but she hadn't said it wasn't either.

"You don't invite people for 8.30 if you don't mean dinner," the little one pointed out, "So I guess it *is* dinner." I guessed so too. If they're not going to feed you they say like, "any time after eight", or they say, "ninish" – they don't say 8.30. On top of that, I had a feeling Mrs. Pomerantz had put a sort of emphasis on the hour. Eight-*thirty,* she'd said, and there'd been a definitely dinnerish edge to her voice . . .

"No," concluded the wife, "it's for dinner. I'm almost certain."

I suggested calling Mrs. Pomerantz and throwing out a feeler, but the wife said no, it wasn't done.

Came Wednesday, and it so happened that we'd both done a lot of running around all day and had only grabbed a sandwich for lunch, so that by evening we were rather hungry, but the little one said better stick it out. "I know Mrs. Pomerantz," thus she, "If she gives you dinner – it's *dinner.*"

I pictured a table with huge platters of shishkebab, turkey,

201

salads, potato crisps and pickles. Just so long as they wouldn't sit around for ages. Keep the chitchat till after dinner, please.

Things didn't look too promising at first. To begin with, no one else had arrived yet, and the Pomerantzes were still dressing. Our worried glances surveyed the living room and found no sign of anything substantial. The equipment was standard: armchairs round a low table, the low table carrying a bowl of salted peanuts, almonds and raisins, some olives, squares of cheese with plastic toothpicks stuck in them, crackers. Could Mrs. Pomerantz have said 9.30 on the phone, not 8.30? Or hadn't she maybe mentioned any time at all and I'd just been imagining things?

"A drink?"

That was Mr. Pomerantz, knotting his tie as he breezed into the room. He offered us a John Collins, which is a great drink made up of a third brandy, a third soda, and a dash of Collins. We'd have welcomed it at any other time, but just then we were rather too turkey-minded to really appreciate it.

"Cheers," said Mr. Pomerantz, "Um . . . have you seen that new Albee play?"

I took a handful of peanuts and tried to enlarge upon the ironic implications of the play's introverted claustrophobic theme, but soon realized I hadn't enough to go on. I mean, what's a few peanuts for a grown man? I thought I'd try olives for a change, but the wife had eaten them all up, along with most of the cheese. By the time we got to the elections, only three raisins and a lone cracker remained.

"Excuse me," said Mrs. Pomerantz, "I'll get some more." She picked up the devastated dishes and went out. We craned our necks to catch a glimpse of the kitchen, maybe something was going on there after all, but the place looked shockingly clean and bare: *nothing* was going on there. Meanwhile some more people had arrived – at 9.15 (?) – and then my stomach suddenly emitted a loud rumble and I thought I'd die of embarrassment.

I started talking at random – about Angola, Uganda, dunno – while beginning to feel slightly sick after my second bowl of peanuts. Not that I have anything against peanuts as such — very wholesome they are, with all those proteins and everything — but they're a pretty poor substitute for turkey and potatoes.

I glanced at the little woman to see how she was getting on. From the looks of her I judged that the almonds and raisins were doing battle with Mr. Collins inside her. I myself switched to cheese, and I believe I swallowed a green plastic toothpick as well. I just couldn't stop any more. Mrs. Pomerantz stared at us hard, exchanged a few words with her husband, then went to the kitchen for fresh supplies.

"Yes," said someone by my side, "but the number of unemployed is rising by leaps and bounds . . . ."

"What do you expect," I retorted, "with a government that's rotten with salt."

Thank God I wasn't speaking very clearly, because my mouth was full of crackers. And anyhow, what did the guy mean telling me about unemployment, when right here in this living room a whole family was starving to death. The peanut bowl was empty again too, and the first signs of panic appeared on the faces of our hosts. Mr. Pomerantz rummaged about in the cupboard for a bit and produced some toffees, which quickly joined the great majority down there. We'd eaten hardly anything since breakfast, as I said, and were reduced to a sort of hand-to-mouth existence now.

The crackers were making such a racket in my mouth, they nearly deafened me from within, and I felt a little dizzy as well. Taking one thing with another, I suppose I had about four lbs. of peanuts, half an olive tree and an ocean of salt inside me. I tried to suppress a fit of hiccups, along with some crazy jingle running through my head about General Smuts, lost his guts, 'cause Pea was crackers and Olive was nuts . . .

Next somebody mentioned Watergate and I nearly gagged. I'd got to the stage where even the thought of water made me sick, let alone food. All right, so let's not think of food, not food, never food . . .

"Please, everybody . . . ."

Mr. Pomerantz threw the door into the next room wide open, revealing a long table resplendent in white damask and . . . plates . . . glasses . . . oh no . . .

And there was Mrs. Pomerantz too. Mrs. Pomerantz with the turkey, the mushroom soup, potato crisps, asparagus, pickles . . .

"Dinner is served . . ."

Ah well, no matter.

'Sleeping's Such a Bore!'

Some children aren't taught to go to sleep on time. Not so our own 11-year-old, Amir, who goes to bed regular as clockwork. It's a real blessing, a child like that: in bed on the dot of 8.30, and up at 7 fresh as a daisy, just like the doctors recommend. A question of discipline.

The weak point in this impressive pedagogic achievement is that there's not a word of truth in it. I mean I'm lying, just like all other parents. Actually, Amir goes to sleep between 11.30 p.m. and 2.15 a.m., depending on the stars in the sky and on TV, and gets up in the morning on all fours. Saturdays and holidays he doesn't get up at all.

It's not that the child refuses to go to bed at 8.30 as the doctors recommend. No, he puts on his pyjamas at 8.30, lies down, even says "Goodnight, dear parents," and only after a certain interval – like, say, a minute, a minute-and-a-half – he gets up again to brush his teeth. Then he has a drink. Then he needs to pee, checks his school-bag, has another drink, watches Mannix, drops in for a chat with the dog, pee no. 2, a bit of nocturnal snail-observation, Jordan TV, kitchen patrol, choco-late biscuit, the clock strikes 2.15, bat-time.

As a result, our Amir looks a bit ethereal. In fact, what with the rings round his eyes he resembles nothing so much as a ghost with glasses. His teacher says he tends to drop under the table in the middle of class, and advises psychotherapy. She also enquires after his bed-time, and we say 8.30 sharp.

For a long time we were bothered by the fact that all the other kids in the neighbourhood go to sleep on time, like

Gideon L.'s bright little girl. Gideon demands strict obedience and rules his daughter with a rod of iron — he's boss at home, and no mistake. Avital turns in at 8.45, regular as clockwork. We saw it ourselves just the other night during a friendly gathering at the Gideon L.'s. At 8.44 Gideon glanced at his watch and said quietly:

"Tally. Bed."

That's all. And Tally gets up, bids us all goodnight, and nips off to her room without a hint of youthful rebellion. There's discipline for you, there's iron. We bury ourselves deep in our armchairs at the thought that at this very moment our son Amir is wandering through the labyrinthine passages of our house like a somnolent Hamlet. However, *However*, a few minutes before the party broke up, at 2.00 G.M.T. to be precise, Tally's door opened suddenly and the obedient but wide-awake girl entered with an armful of newspapers and asked:

"Anybody seen the Friday supplement?"

Gideon L. blushed down to the strip under his wristwatch, and since that evening we, too, tell visitors that our children go to bed like clockwork.

The truth is that we know quite well what keeps Amir from falling asleep on time. The virus of insomnia got into his system during the Yom Kippur War, when the radio broadcast all-night news from the front and we hadn't the heart to let our son miss the military spokesman's announcements. A biological blunder, for which we pay with all-night wanderings, teeth-brushings, pees, snails, bats.

Once I staggered into the kitchen at 2.25 and caught him with a bottle of illicit Cola.

"Why aren't you asleep, son?"

"Sleeping's such a bore."

I offered instructive examples from the animal world, which drops off at nightfall as one animal, but he countered with the owl, declaring that this fly-by-night had been his ideal since youth, i.e., since the day before yesterday. I considered spanking him till he'd go to sleep, but my wife intervened because she can't bear to see me hit her babies. Consequently I just stood and screamed: "Amir, go to sleep! *Sleep!*" but he crossword puzzles till three.

Then we consulted a psychotherapist, and he warned against breaking the child's spirit. "Let Nature take its course," said the man, and we gave Nature a chance, but Nature didn't take it. When I found Amir drawing airplanes with coloured chalk one night at 3.30 I lost my temper and rang up the permissive psychotherapist then and there. The clear treble of a small child answered, "My Daddy's asleep."

Salvation came with the Passover holiday.

Not right away, since on the first schoolless night our boy hit the sack at 3.55 a.m. (three fifty-five *ante meridiem*), and the night after he didn't shut an eye till 4.20. His stormy night-life disturbed our own slumbers as well, because we just couldn't lie there quietly counting sheep while our little lamb gambolled all over the place. To make matters worse, we discovered that his hours kept getting later and later every day. My wife wanted to spank him so he'd go to sleep on time, but I didn't let her because I can't stand seeing her beat my kids.

And then — eureka!

"Ephraim," said the wife sitting up in bed at the crack of one dawn, "What time is it?"

"Ten past five," I yawned.

We could hear our little owl tripping down the passage, presumably out on a biscuit raid or something.

"Ephraim," mused the little woman, "let's admit that we can't get Amir *back* to normal bedtime hours, so what do you say we try and move him *forward* to them?"

The idea seemed pretty revolutionary at first glance, but it proved itself educationwise. During all that vacation we gave Amir's glued eyes carte blanche. Nay, we positively encouraged him not to sleep at all.

"You go to bed when you feel like it," we told him. "It's good for you." Our son cooperated. Preliminary results follow:

On the third day of treatment, Amir fell asleep at 5.30 in the morning and woke at one in the afternoon.

On the eighth day, he drifted off at 9.50 a.m. and rose at 6.30 p.m.

On day 13 he lay him down at 3.30 p.m. and got up at midnight, full of beans.

On day 16 he fell asleep at six in the evening and got up with the birds.

On the last day of vacation, Amir finally caught up with himself. He fell asleep at 8.30 like clockwork and woke up on the dot of 7, just as the doctors recommend. Thank God, the child's recovered his health and gone back to a regular life at last. Unless I'm lying again.

Come Back Goldshtik, All is Forgiven

The question of who asked Shlomo Goldshtik to paint our bedroom still rages in our family. My wife claims I used to make her nights hell because of the smudges on the ceiling, whereas I only remember her "Look at those walls, just look at those walls."

Anyway, one morning the little one caught sight of two housepainters with ladders and buckets on the Seligs' doorstep, and at once waylaid them with an invitation to do our bedroom. They – Shlomo Goldshtik and his helper Mahmud – said yes, they'd come, Thursday at 7.30 a.m. The question of payment was left open but we handed over a IL.200 advance for plastic paint.

They came on Thursday at 7.10. Mahmud spread our furniture daintily with the foreign press, while the floor received full coverage from *The Jerusalem Post*. Next they put up a multicoloured step-ladder, tied handkerchiefs round their faces against the dust, and rubbed down three walls and half a ceiling. Then they vanished.

Goldshtik and Mahmud, that is, not the ceiling, the ladder, the papers, or the dust under our feet. At first we thought they'd probably gone off to buy paint and such, but after some three days we grew restless. It's hard to sleep in a sandpapered room. It's even harder to get up and find yourself ankle-deep in dust, on account of Goldshtik having asked us particularly not to sweep it up as it would constitute a natural defence, so to speak, against dripping paint. So we didn't sweep it up, but where was Goldshtik?

"He looked such a solid kind of man," mused the wife on the fourth day, "whoever would have thought he'd evaporate like that?"

She called on the Seligs and found their place in the same state as ours: orphaned step-ladder, buckets, dust, and no Goldshtik. The two painters had only worked half a day for them too, and Mahmud had just asked did they have milk in the house as he'd like a glass please every morning, before they sallied out into the darkness at noon.

What's more, they, the Seligs, had gone to visit the Friedlanders in Ramat Gan last Saturday, and as soon as they entered the living room under an open step-ladder they had seen "Goldshtik was here" written all over the place. It seemed they had started work in Ramat Gan about ten minutes after they'd begun on us. Mahmud had shown up a week later, explained that his and Goldshtik's wives were in hospital, rubbed down two doorposts, and was never seen again.

"Ephraim," declared the wife, "Those painters are nuts."

It turned out that they weren't nuts at all. A quick spot-check revealed Goldshtik traces in no less than eight flats in our neighbourhood alone. Apparently this industrious labourer simply hates to turn down an order in the burning summer season, so he shows up everywhere on the dot, pitches his ladder on the premises, rubs a little off here, slaps a little on there, and decamps in pursuit of new hunting-grounds.

At one place they'd waited for him in a wasteland of paint-pots and rubble for three months, till Goldshtik popped in suddenly one evening at six, inspected the walls and announced: "Dry."

Then he put on another coat and vanished for six months. He has many customers, has Shlomo Goldshtik. He never leaves an address behind: he's a strict don't-call-me-I'll-call-you type. Mahmud says nothing at all, only smokes cigarette stubs while stirring the paint.

Their craftsmanship is first-rate. That's just what's so maddening — that there's no one as good as Goldshtik if he comes, especially at doing doors and lintels. It *is* rather a nuisance that he leaves all the doors in the house up between two chairs, though you can of course sit on them after they've dried. Plenty of Goldshtik D.P.s have been dining off horizontal doors for months.

The other day we went to see the Spiegels and found they had adjusted quite cheerfully to the ladder-and-bucket arrangement in the corner of their *salon*. They say it's like pop art, don't you think?

We fell to discussing the world of Shlomo Goldshtik. He's a nice guy, really, very polite and all. Rather tired-looking, no? Well, with all the travelling he has to do, what d'you expect? It's true we don't know how he moves about, as no one has ever seen him arrive. He's just there, suddenly, complete with ladders and Mahmud.

"He probably lives in a van," suggested Friedlander, "so as to be mobile."

He's as hard to pin down as a roving diplomat. The owner of one of his abandoned properties once tried to recall his features for a police identikit and failed. The two of them always wear handkerchiefs, remember?

Hoodlums?

"No," said Spiegel at our general assembly, "he just doesn't want to lose his sources of income."

We, the children of his step-ladder, number 110 full members at the moment. Our record-holder is a distinguished writer with a ceiling of 18 months, as shown by the date of the papers on his floor. Comparing notes, we found that Goldshtik generally rubs down at least a wall and a half, drinks a glass of milk, moves the ladder into the other room, and skedaddles.

We voted to call our abandoned-customers association "The Knights of the Door Table", and settled down to discuss administrative matters, like how does Gold do his vanishing shtik, what does he live on, how did he manage to collect such a flock of ladders?

"He must have a computer," Friedlander, our chairman, observed, "He could never be so efficient without one."

As for his means, Goldshtik subsists on advances, since he never gets as far as payday.

According to the annual report of our executive committee, Goldshtik started off one typical morning (May 29) with seven (!) new apartments, one of them in Upper Nazareth. They also say Mahmud was spotted the other day playing ping-pong on the beach while doing the doorposts in Herzliya.

"The man's a genius," my wife declared one evening amid the buckets in our bedroom. "He might have made something of himself, been a great painter . . ."

A painter in the neck! I was getting a bit sick of this unto dust returning every day of my life. The little woman took it in better spirit, and even sewed a pretty curtain for the ladder because you could never tell, maybe Goldshtik would come back some day after all.

"He won't," says Erna Selig, "He's had plastic surgery done and gone into hiding."

Anyhow, "The Knights of the Door Table" have laid deep plans. We're in constant touch with one another on our customer-to-customer hot line. As soon as Goldshtik is spotted anywhere we'll close in with dogs. "Operation Michelangelo." Friedlander will hail him over the loudspeakers: "The place is surrounded, Goldshtik. Surrender!" This will be followed by lengthy negotiations. Goldshtik will promise to finish the living room and come back tomorrow for the doors if we give him a car with chauffeur. Not on your life, Goldshtik! The beleaguered artist will offer Mahmud as hostage. Nyet! But he needs turpentine. We'll get it for you, Goldy! Towards evening a can of milk is slipped in. At dark Goldshtik moves the ladder to the bathroom and turns out the lights . . .

Huh, pipedreams. When the ultimatum has run out and our forces storm the house, we'll find it empty of Goldshtik. He'll already be doing a wall in Holon, and our troops will retreat step by bloody step-ladder and go home in despair and kick the bucket.

For Whom the Bins Bang

When does a person sleep best?

The answer, according to scientific research, is up to 5.25 in the morning. Till then the man-in-the-street is in bed and sound asleep, but at 5.25 he wakes up screaming to the sounds of an earthquake. If he listens well, though, he hears that the noise is actually a mixture of several things, such as a surprise air raid, a buffalo stampede, a roll of thunder and the rumble of a dozen tanks, with the roar of a wounded Tarzan rushing to the aid of his son . . .

At 5.25 in the morning.

Every sleeper reacts in his own way. Some bury themselves full fathom five under their pillows and pray softly. Others leap out of bed and start pacing the room. I myself attack the little woman and wrestle with her till she manages to turn on the light and persuade me that I'm not having a nightmare . . .

It all only lasts some 90 seconds. Then a booming male voice emits something that sounds like "hoo-hoh!" — and the nightmare moves off down the street.

"It beats me how so few people can manage to make so much noise," my neighbour Felix Selig told me from his open window one morning at 5.25, "It really does."

We looked down at the small but tightly-knit crew below, made up of the driver of the garbage truck, one fellow towering on top of the heap, and two more dragging the bins out of our courtyard. Merely four sanitation workers going about their business, you'd say, but their noise technique is extremely sophisticated, and worked out to the last detail.

The man at the wheel drives exclusively in top gear, the bins are dragged rat-tat-tat over the paving stones of the courtyard, and the draggers themselves argue so loudly and furiously you feel that in a moment they'll drop everything — bang! — and be at each other's throats.

But no, when you listen closely you realize they're just having a friendly chat, even if by some unwritten rule of the game nobody can start talking before the two big-draggers are well inside our courtyard, at about 30 paces from the truck. Only then may they turn and bellow at the driver:

"YOHO!" they go, "WHAT DID YOU DO LAST NIGHT, HA?"

The driver sticks his head out and trumpets into the rosy dawn:

"YOHO! WE STAYED HOME AND WATCHED THE TELLY, WE DID. HOW 'BOUT YOU?"

"GRABBED A BANG-BANG MOVIE, WE DID! LOTSA ACTION! HOT STUFF THAT MOVIE WAS!"

Those of our neighbours whose windows face the backyard claim that the two draggers occasionally talk shop over the bin between them too:

"BRRR!" one of them roars from half a yard's distance at his colleague, "WEIGHS A BLOODY TON TODAY, THIS BIN DOES, HA?"

"YOU BET, CHUM! THEY EATS GOOD ON THIS STREET, THEY DOES!"

Mrs. Kalaniyot, who lives bang above the bins' parking lot, and who is rather jittery as a consequence, flung her window wide one morning and shrieked at the rioters:

"Quiet, for God's sake! quiet! Why do you make such a row here every night?"

"HELL, LADY," one dragger roared back politely, "THIS YOU CALL NIGHT? IT'S HALF PAST FIVE IN THE MORNING, IT IS!"

"I'll call the Police!" Felix Selig joined in the chorus, whereupon the four sanitarians nearly split their sides laughing:

"SURE!" they called to Felix, "AND WHERE YOU

214

FIGURE YOU'LL FIND A COP AT HALF PAST FIVE IN THE MORNING, HA?"

They are cheerful fellows, these four municipal gentlemen, sturdy Israelis who'll stand up for what they believe in, and who won't take orders from anyone. One day I got in touch with the Sanitation Department to ask couldn't they do something about these earthquakes at the crack of dawn.

"I know what you mean," said the department chief sympathetically, "It's the same at my place every morning. Terrible, isn't it?"

Next we sent a petition to the Authorities, signed by every householder on the block, saying couldn't they ask the four crackers of dawn to please not drop the bins from anything over two yards. We got no reply. The Zieglers' help, a girl by name of Ethroga, told us we were wasting our time, she lived right next to one of the four, the one lording it on top of the heap, and she knew for a fact that two Ministers had tried to take action, and in the end had been forced to resign and go back to their kibbutz.

To top it all, the environmentalists keep warning us – us! – against the evil consequences of too much noise. The damage to people's brain structure, they say, will be irreparable, and may well be passed on to their progeny...

We could picture our descendants, deaf, dumb and brainless to the last great-grandchild, sending us a reproachful look and loping off into the forests. No, we resolved, something has to be done! But what, ha?

If you can't beat'em, said Ziegler, join 'em, and he had a point there, because though we'd never considered actually joining them at the bin-bang, we did feel a bit guilty. I mean, here were these four stalwarts slaving away, while we spoilt bourgeois lay snoozing in our beds till 5.25 in the morning. We decided, therefore, to try the psychological approach, money was no object...

Two days later we overheard the following dialogue:

"YOHO!" – this from the Lord of the Heap – "MORNINGS GETTING BLOODY COLD, HA?"

"YOHO!" — from the yard — "SO PUT ON A SWEATER, CHUM!"

"A SWEATER! A SWEATER, HE SAYS! WHERE YOU FIGURE I'LL TAKE A SWEATER FROM, WHERE?"

That was our cue. We acted — for our own sake, for the sake of our great-grandchildren, for peace in the Middle East. We all pitched in, and Mrs. Kalaniyot went and bought a splendid woollen sweater in the largest size available, and Felix Selig, led by Ethroga, took it to the Lord of the Heap's address. The delegation solemnly presented him with it on behalf of all the neighbours, with expressions of goodwill all round and peace on earth in the morning. The Lord was touched, thanked Felix over and over, and said he couldn't wait to tell his chums . . .

Next morning at 5.25 we jumped out of bed in a fright.

"YOHO!" we heard the Lord thundering from his heap, "HERE'S WHERE THEY BOUGHT ME THIS SWEATER, THEY DID! HERE'S WHERE!"

"REAL NICE OF 'EM!" the driver yelled back, "REAL NICE, BLESS 'EM!"

Then came the final lordly crash. With his heart swelling under the new sweater, the Lord flung the bin up in a great joyous arc. It came down, hit a second bin placed on the edge of the fence, and the two of them clattered along the pavement like so many cannon balls. I've been deaf in my left ear ever since, with the result that I now sleep quite well on my other side.

Passing on the Knowledge

"Daddy!"

That's how my children address me as a rule. This time it was Amir standing in the doorway of my study, where I'm trying to work.

"Daddy," my blue-eyed boy says to me, "does the earth revolve round the sun?"

"Yes," Daddy replies, "Of course."

"How d'you know?"

That's the effect of all those space-flights, I guess. The kid is out to conquer the solar system. Good for you, my boy.

"Everybody knows that," I explain patiently, "We learned it at school."

"What did you learn?"

My brain shifts to low gear. What *did* we learn, as a matter of fact? All I remember of my cosmology is the incontrovertible fact that our physics teacher wore a bow-tie and would sometimes talk for minutes on end with his eyes shut. He had buck teeth. Didn't we call him "Horse?" Think so. Must check up on that some time.

"So how d'you know?"

"Don't be silly!" I chide my son. "There's proofs. Like if the sun revolved round us, they'd call it the 'Earth System' and not the Solar . . ."

I can see his attention wandering. I'll have to give him some tangible evidence before he gets any funny ideas. He's a redhead, after all.

"Look," I say, picking up a rubber eraser from my desk,

"Let's say this is the moon, and this box of thumb-tacks is the earth . . ."

The desk lamp naturally becomes the sun. Daddy turns the eraser and the tacks gracefully round the lamp, slowly, round and round . . .

"See the shadow, little blockhead? When the eraser is right in the middle, the box is all in shadow . . ."

"Yeah," my son comments, "And it's also in shadow if you turn the lamp and the box stays put."

Pah!

"Use your head!" I shout at the boy. "If the lamp turned, then the shadow would go all to one side . . ."

And, sure enough, the plug flies out of the socket and there be darkness. I bend down, and all the thumb-tacks of the universe scatter over the floor, on account of the centrifugal force, dammit!

"You bum!"

One of his socks is always slipping, I've never seen such a sloppy kid! As I crawl about the floor gathering thumb-tacks — ouch! — I remember Galileo, who discovered all that stuff about the sun and all, at the royal court of . . . of . . . some king. I know, because I've just been to this play. *Si muove*, he said there. A good play, some first-rate acting, and there were lots of stairs on the stage. I go over to the window and glance up at the sky to see if something is moving up there, but no, only clouds . . .

"Go back to your room," I tell my son, "and think over your stupid question *again!*"

Amir, offended, goes off to his room. I pounce on the encyclopaedia: — Columbus — Copenhagen — Copernicus, Nicolas, German astronomer (1473–1543). They ramble on about him for half a page, but when it comes to explaining about what moves around what, and why — nothing. Looks like the encyclopaedia editors couldn't remember anything either. I saunter casually into my son's room and place my warm hand upon his flaming locks.

"All right now?"

"No," says the brat. "Dad, you haven't got a clue!" He means me, *I* haven't got a clue. The bloody cheek! I raise my voice to quote the actor in that play:

"Remember what Galileo told his judges? And yet it does move!"

"Okay, so it moves," thus my son, "but not round the sun."

"Then round what? Round the cat?"

I'm beginning to sweat. My prestige is at stake! "Just a minute. Telephone," I shout quickly and hurry out. In a dark corner of the living room I surreptitiously call up Bruno, who is a biochemist or something.

"Listen," I whisper into the receiver, "how do we know that the earth revolves round the sun?"

A brief silence, then Bruno asks in a whisper why am I whispering. I say I'm hoarse, come on, why does it turn, eh?

"That's what we learnt at school," this so-called biochemist stutters, "I think it's the four seasons that prove it . . . especially summer . . ."

"Yeah," I scoff, "You'll get the same seasons if the lamp turns and the box stays put."

I ring up Dolly as well. She studied law once. She remembers something about 'Fouchet's Pendulum' from her physics lessons. They hung it from a church tower somewhere, and it drew lines in the sand on the floor or something . . .

I'm beginning to sympathize with the Inquisition. Here's this upstart going around like a bloody town crier shouting: It moves! It moves! "How do you know, sir?" "I can feel it in my bones." Like hell you can! And Fouchet, too! Just a lousy French cop! What's the matter with everybody? I creep back to my study and the daily grind. Where's that eraser?

"Daddy!"

Redhead in the doorway.

"Well," he says, "so what's turning?"

A deep weariness comes over me. My back hurts too. You can't go on fighting all your life.

"Everything," I mumble, "Everything turns . . ."

"So you say the sun goes round us?"

"They're still arguing about that. Anything's possible nowadays. We'll see."

I look at him and roar at the top of my voice:

"Pull up your socks!"

Bum!

How Napoleon was Defeated

The sun rising over the field of battle found the Emperor bent over his maps in the palace living room, his faithful marshals standing behind him in reverent silence: the greatest military leader of all time was laying his strategy for the crucial confrontation with Europe's kings.

His months of exile on Elba had made no change in the Emperor's gallant mien — only his hair had thinned slightly, and a few silver threads glistened at his temples. An occasional boom of distant cannon told of Blücher's Prussian troops marching on Waterloo . . .

The silken curtains fluttered in the morning breeze. The world held its breath.

"Napoleon, come and eat your breakfast!"

Bella, the Emperor's third wife, popped her head through the door. A handsome woman, her hair done up in a kerchief, a dustcloth in her hand. She had married Napoleon on Elba, and people had congratulated him and said she'd make him an excellent Jewish wife.

"Nu, Napoleon," she said, "It'll get cold if you don't eat it now. Your friends here won't run away." She turned to the marshals with a sigh. "Same thing every time," she complained, "I ask him — does he want to eat or doesn't he. I just want he should tell me: yes or no. So I cook and all — and then when it's ready monsieur has got something else to do and me I can wait with my food. And I can't just keep warming it up, it spoils it. And now my maid's left me too and I'm stuck with the kid and all. Napoleon, come and eat immediately."

"A second," muttered the great General, marking a change in the battle formation on his map, "Just a second."

The roar of cannon grew louder beyond the hills. Marshal Ney glanced at his watch with a worried frown: Wellington's artillery was getting the range ...

"I'm out on my feet," Bella pointed out, "You drop your things all over the place, and all I got to do all day is tidy up after you. And take that hand out of your coat! I keep telling you it makes it baggy, and the stuff doesn't iron well. My husband," she turned to the marshals again, "has got some habits, I tell you – I'm surprised his other wives stood it. Napoleon! Breakfast!"

"Right away," said the Emperor, and looked round at the tense faces of his officers, "Blücher and Wellington will try to join forces," he explained, "and we've got to prevent that at all costs – we *must* drive a wedge between them."

"It's getting cold!"

"We shall attack in one hour's time!"

Now General Cambron's heavy tread was heard outside, bounding up the marble steps two at a time ...

"No, no!" cried Bella, stopping him at the door, "First take those boots off. I don't want mud all over my nice clean floors!"

General Cambron took his boots off and remained in his stocking-feet like all the marshals in the room.

"I wouldn't mind if I still had my maid," Bella explained, "but she up and left me yesterday. I warned Nappy that I didn't like the looks of her but he didn't listen, because to him anything's more important than what happens in his own home. So now I'm without a maid, and tomorrow is Friday already, and I've no time to even look for a new one because of this battle of yours. So if any of you marshals hears of a nice modest girl who can do the cooking and look after the kid, let me know, but don't send me a Corsican because they jabber all day."

"Very well, Your Imperial Highness" – General Cambron

saluted, and handed the Emperor an urgent message.

Napoleon read it and blanched.

"Gentlemen," he whispered, "Fouchet has gone over to the enemy. Fouchet! What now?"

"Breakfast," suggested Bella, "It's getting cold on your plate."

She went off to warm it up again, and Napoleon began giving out his final orders.

"The fate of the world will be decided *here!*" — his finger swooped down on the map — "Now then, if this maid attacks from the east we shall regroup at this point and . . ."

"Napoleon!" came a voice from the other room, "How do you want your egg?"

"I don't care."

"Soft?"

"Yes,"

"Then say so."

The Man of Destiny pulled on his boots, picked up his hat, and every line in his face bespoke determination to win this — the Battle of Nations.

"Gentlemen! For France!"

"For France!" thundered the marshals with drawn swords, "For the Emperor!"

"Nappy" — Bella stuck her head through the door — "The kid's calling for you."

"Your Highness," Marshal Murat whispered, "the enemy is at the gate!"

"Yes, but it's me who'll be stuck here all day with a child *nudzhing* for his daddy — not you," said Bella, "I'm sure nothing terrible will happen if Napoleon comes and gives his little boy a kiss before he goes to work."

"Where is he?"

"On the potty."

The Emperor rushed out.

"It's that I've got no maid," Bella explained, "and all this palace to keep clean. You! How many times have I asked you to use an ashtray! . . ."

223

Napoleon marched through the living room on his way out.

"What do I say if anyone asks for you?" said Bella.

"I'm at the Battle of Waterloo."

"When'll you be back?"

"Don't know."

"But I've got to say something if people ask, no? Will you be home for lunch?"

"If I can make it."

"What do you want I shall cook?"

"Whatever."

"Stuffed *kishkeh?*"

"Yes."

"Then say so."

The Emperor left.

"You haven't finished your breakfast!" Bella called after him from the window, "And remember: a maid! And don't be late!"

The Emperor's proud figure retreated along the narrow path leading to the fields of Waterloo. Bella took a rag and began cleaning up the mud from all over her nice clean floors — doing it herself because she had no maid. The smell of gunpowder wafted in through the window, flashes of cannon fire lit up the trees. It was in those minutes that the armies of Blücher and Wellington joined forces, and the Battle of Waterloo was won by two men who had gone to war alone, and left their devoted wives very far behind indeed.

A Brontosaurus in Every Drawer

They say childhood is a happy time, and it is — but for whom? I always thought the answer was toyshops, but now I think it's Mrs. Frisch. I'll explain myself.

Some months ago an unknown genius discovered that in the era of TV, kids are no longer willing to look at picture books unless they have to stick in the pictures themselves and can leave glue on the carpet. The result was an album called "The Wonderful World", all 46 pages of it. The pages are large, and each has space for nine coloured pictures, which you buy at Mrs. Frisch's on the corner — three pictures for ten cents.

The album is very educational, with pictures of just about every wonder in the world, living or dead. It ranges from the solar system to prehistoric monsters, and from the Pyramids to the most modern printing presses with a capacity of 100,000 stick-in pictures a minute.

And those presses work 24 hours a day.

For my son Amir.

* * *

The point, you see, is that the little pictures come in sealed envelopes, and a child buying them from Mrs. Frisch is obliged to buy a whole lot of pigs in a poke before he finds the one lion that's missing in his album. This plays hell with the family budget, but the child himself develops a sound stock-market instinct, as he goes to school every morning with a schoolbag full of pictures for swopping.

The hitch is that by now Amir has got hold of a lion's share of the lions. For the last six months he's been investing all his savings in pictures. His room is ankle-deep in wonders, and you can't open a drawer in the house without at least a dozen brontosauruses jumping out at you. I asked him about it once. "Amir," I said, "this album of yours is bursting at the seams already. Why do you go on buying pictures?"

"Just in case."

All I can say in his defence is that he hasn't the faintest idea what he's sticking in his album, since he never bothers to read the text underneath. What he knows about centrifugal force, for instance, is that Nicky gave him a swordfish and two Boeings for it. It's a plain case of overkill. Yes, and on top of that he steals.

* * *

I found out about it one day as I was taking a nap, when I opened one eye and caught my ginger boy with his hand in the pocket of my pants like a regular Minister of Finance.

"Hey!" I shouted, wide awake, "What're you doing there?"

"Looking for money," he answered matter of factly, "Nicky needs a wall-eyed pike."

"So?" I asked, "And can't Nicky steal from his own daddy?"

"No. His daddy gets mad."

That made sense. We talked it over, the culprit's mother and I, and decided there was no point emigrating just now, the album would catch up with us anywhere. Instead we called a parents' meeting with Teacher Hemda, who rates the number of pictures hoarded by her pupils at between three and four million per class.

"The only solution I can think of," she announced, "would be to drop a hint to the tax people that some album-maker in this country is making a fortune . . ."

I told them Amir was stealing. They only laughed at me.

"My son carried out an armed robbery last week," one unhappy father said, "Tried to do his grandpa in with a hammer, just because he wouldn't give the kid money for a mastodon."

The grandpa has rallied. Some parents suggested banning

the sale of glue, and one father, a Mr. Frisch, said why not fight it the way Denmark did pornography: swamp the kids with pictures till they got sick of the sight of them. Good idea. Next morning I went out and bought a whole basketful of pictures at Mrs. Frisch's, among them a gory "Victims of the Aztecs", and "Leonardo's First Flying Machine."

Amir made short work of the basket, and had its contents scattered over the lower regions of the house in less than no time. He kept to the lower regions because a few days ago our char opened the top door of the kitchen cabinet and was buried alive under a shower of wonders. The char has rallied. The Danish method doesn't seem to work, though: however many pictures I get him, Amir just holds out his hand and says: "More."

Even his looks have undergone a change. His eyes have narrowed, his cheeks grown sort of baggy, and the little woman declares he's gradually turning into a hamster. A hamster, according to the dictionary, is "a large rat-like rodent with cheek-pouches for carrying grain to its winter storage". Exactly. Amir to a T.

* * *

Yesterday I shut myself up in my room, swept a bit of Greek mythology to the floor, and sat down to read the paper. Suddenly I feel someone breathing down my neck: my little hamster-boy with a fistful of small, black-and-white pictures.

"Look – Giora Spiegel" – showing me a dozen portraits of the great football star – "and I've got 21 Peles and five Bobby Moores already too."

The World of Sport had arrived – the album of the competition.

And that's all for now. If you never hear from me again, you may try and look for me in our living room, under the halfbacks and the centre forwards.

Looking a Gift-Horse in the Eye

Of all the Jewish holidays, Chanuka is the worst. It's not the dripping candles I mind, or the potato-latkes giving me indigestion, it's that Chanuka is gift-giving time. Again, it's not the money, it's that I never know what to buy for the little woman. She, I might add, has the same problem. Thinking back on it, I remember that three years ago she bought me two antique foils for Chanuka, and I bought her a cute little table lamp. By the way, I don't fence. Two years ago she surprised me with the complete works of Lope de Vega, and I gave her a cute little table lamp. I don't read Spanish. Last year was really tough: the little woman produced a Lebanese hookah, and I got her quite a cute little table lamp.

I don't smoke.

This year we started worrying way ahead of time, because what more could we buy each other? We already had every-thing. Three weeks before Chanuka someone told me he'd seen the little one drop in on a real-estate agent. We have a joint bank account. I broke out in a cold sweat. I decided to appeal to her common sense: "Look, honey-bunch," I said, "We've got to put a stop to this or we'll both go mad. I worry, you worry, and if you ask me — I don't see what Chanuka has got to do with presents in the first place. It's all very well about this oil lasting eight days and all, but it's still no reason why I should buy you a dress, is it? I don't buy you a flat for Purim, do I? Now then, let's us two intelligent grownups cut out all this nonsense and promise each other not to buy presents this Chanuka. What say?"

The wife threw her arms about me and said she'd never thought I had it in me. She said she'd thought of it herself, but she just hadn't had the nerve to bring it up. Oh dear, what relief, oh, what a load off her mind. We laughed and kissed, and that was the end of the gift problem.

* * *

The following morning it dawned on me that I still didn't know what to buy the little woman for Chanuka. My first idea was a cute little table lamp, and then I thought perhaps not, she already had quite a collection of them. But if no table lamp, all that remained was a diamond tiara, that being the only thing she didn't have yet. I put an ad in the paper — Wanted: a secondhand tiara in good condition. I received two offers with prices. So all right — no tiara. Back to square one.

A fortnight before D-day the wife came home with a box under her arm. I tore the lid off in a raging fury: milk powder. Just to be sure I took a sieve and sifted the contents for hidden cuff-links and such, but it was what it seemed — milk powder pure and innocent. I was rather jittery by then, so next morning I went to the bank to check our account, and nearly got a fit: the little woman had withdrawn 2,600 pounds, leaving only 80 cents, which I took out at once. God, was I angry! All right, I thought, just you wait, my dear! I'm going to buy you such a mink that we'll be ruined for good. I'll run up debts, I'll take to drink, what-do-I-mean-drink, hash — just because you can't stick to your promises.

I returned home and just managed to catch the wife sneaking in by the back door with a large parcel. I snatched it out of her hands and — there! A dozen shirts! I took a pair of scissors and cut them savagely to shreds.

"Snip!" I yelled, "And snap! And that'll teach you to break your word!"

The little one, who'd only been returning my clean shirts from the laundry, defended herself indignantly. "We should trust each other," she said, "That's the whole point of a marriage: mutual trust!" I said by all means, and what had she done with those 2,600 pounds? Oh, she said, settled her monthly bill at the hairdresser's. I felt like a perfect rotter. How could I have accused this model wife of mine of wasting money on rubbish?

We smiled at each other, and the whole problem seemed pretty childish all of a sudden. Hadn't we been making mountains out of molehills?

We shook hands like two conspirators, and life went back to normal.

* * *

The people at the shoe store told me they could only make a pair of snake-skin slippers for my wife if I got them an old shoe of hers, but when I was hunting under the bed for one, the little woman pounced:

"Aha!" she cried. "The perfect husband! Gives his wife a lecture about mutual trust, and then goes and stabs her in the back! And me I believed you, more fool I, and I can just imagine the scene you'd have made because here was Chanuka and I hadn't got you a present! Bah!"

All right! We placed our right hands on one of the cute little table lamps and then and there swore a solemn oath that we wouldn't buy each other a thing this Chanuka. That night I slept well for the first time in months.

* * *

Next morning I kept an eye on the wife, and when she went out I followed her — all the way to Jaffa, where she entered some shop. I crept over for a look: Corsets and Bras. Good. Tonight was Chanuka, and she couldn't do much harm between now and then. On my way home, I called in at Wexler's the antiquarian and bought the little one a Chinese vase for 1,860 cash, but fate willed otherwise. Why do those damned bus-drivers brake so abruptly? I tried gluing it but there were too many splinters and too little time left. Deep in my heart I was glad: so I wouldn't be committing a breach of trust after all.

I found the little one at home dressed in her best black and glowing with excitement. Neatly laid out on the table were, among other things, an electric razor, a dozen ball-points, a new typewriter ribbon, a tin of ski wax, a caged canary, six pairs of socks, a cute little table lamp (?), her photo for my desk, a desk, paperclips, and a record-player (the which she'd bought second-hand from the Corsets-and-Bras woman).

I stood there with a sheepish grin on my face and stuttered like an idiot. The little one stared at me in utter disbelief, then burst out crying.

"You don't love me," she sobbed, "Tonight is Chanuka and you didn't buy me even one lousy little present! Go away! I never want to see you again, boohoo . . ."

I put a hand in my pocket and drew out the gold watch. Silly darling.

Hairborne

The Yom Kippur War left an indelible mark on the soul of my son Amir. Under the impact of historic events, the child stopped brushing his teeth and hardened in his refusal to have his hair cut. At a time when our men were fighting at the front, ran his argument, we shouldn't bother with trivialities. We weren't unduly worried by the toothbrush slow-down, because yellow is beautiful too. But Amir's flowing locks had reached his shoulders and were red into the bargain, and they covered his eyes till he looked like nothing so much as a Tibetan terrier in winter. There's this, though: dogs have a keen sense of smell to compensate for their weak eyesight, whereas Amir had to grope his way along by touch.

"Ephraim," said his mama, "your son looks like Mowgli, the jungle boy who was brought up by wolves . . ."

The little wolf-cub, however, stuck to his ideological principles: he wouldn't cut his hair till we had peace with the Arab countries. I suggested, by way of alternative, that maybe he'd *cut* his hair till peace came and *stop* when it did, but he wouldn't budge. We found ourselves in a rather delicate position as parents, since we're always reluctant to impose our will on the child by force because he bites.

Not that life had been much easier before the war. Amir began hating all scissors when he was two, at which age he fell in with the anti-anti spirit of yeah-yeah youth the world over. Since then he's mourned each hair that falls from his head as if it were mink or something. Once we managed to drag him to the barber's with the diplomatic promise that they'd just trim the borders a bit and afterwards we'd make straight for the nearest toyshop . . .

"The son of a self-respecting writer," said Mama with incontrovertible logic, "can't walk around looking like a shaggy dog story."

Amir sat down in the barber's chair with the air of a condemned man. I think he even asked for a priest. Anyway, when it was all over he looked at last like a nice child from a good home. He had only kicked the barber twice and promised to do him in the first chance he got. We didn't interfere, though, because it seemed a choice between barber and barbarian.

And then came this war with its moral justifications.

After the crossing of the Canal, Amir pointed triumphantly to the soldiers on TV:

"See? They don't cut their hair either!"

It's true there can't have been many wars fought by soldiers with such long hair as the short war of that October. I suppose it was due to the haste with which the reserves were called up. Anyway, the tangled manes of our brave young Samsons stuck out in all directions from under their helmets, without the least consideration for Amir's parents. To judge by their screen appearances, they didn't seem to have much time to shave, either. No wonder the child was affected.

Gramps tried economic pressure:

"If you let your hair be cut just a bit," he coaxed his grandson, "I'll take out a subscription to the Encyclopaedia of Wild Animals for you."

"Nope," said Amir, "Hair."

Like a wild animal. We offered a bike. The child vacillated briefly and decided: nyet.

At that point we realized he meant it.

The reader may ask why didn't we snip his tresses in his sleep by way of "Parents be upon thee, Amir," but we aren't that philistine and besides, he sleeps with a ruler under his pillow. We know, we tried cutting his hair in his sleep.

Since the ruler incident, our son has grown even more

inflexible. He tosses his hair deliberately into his eyes and makes a great show of bumping into the furniture a couple of times a day. I decide it's time for a man-to-man talk, as the family code prescribes.

"Why do you object to having your hair cut, my boy?"

"I like it long."

"Why?"

" 'Cause that's what it grows for. It's how God meant it to be."

"So according to you we shouldn't cut our nails either."

"Exactly."

M'm, that *was* a rather unhappy example. I decide on a different approach.

"If you wear your hair long," I venture, "people'll think you're a girl."

"So what's wrong with girls?"

"Nothing, Except that you aren't one."

"So you want to punish me for it?"

That's how useful and constructive *our* little talk was. The wife and I held a closed meeting in the kitchen and resolved upon drastic measures: to cut his hair under an anaesthetic. It seemed a simple enough operation tactically: I'd grab Amir from behind and hold his arms like a one-man Starsky and Hutch team, while Mummy thrust a chloroform-soaked rag under his nose. We'd have ten minutes to finish the job with the scissors. We might even use the opportunity to clean his teeth. And change a sock.

We don't see what else we can do, except perhaps comply with our mini-hippie's condition and make peace with the Arabs. Come to think of it, that may well be the easiest solution.

Frankie

One day towards the end of the 'thirties, two great impresarios met somewhere in a New York suburb. They were both slightly tipsy. "Listen," bragged the one in the grey suit, "I bet I could turn anyone you like into a movie idol." The other fellow sniggered, "Nuts," he said, "hooey!" They bet each other then and there that the one in the grey suit would make a world-famous star out of the first guy who happened along. Mr. Grey Suit was out of luck. The first passer-by was a runt of a youngster, with the build of a mouse-excused-from-physical-training, and with a raisin for a face. The first impresario broke out laughing. "Oh well," said Grey Suit, "a bet's a bet . . ."

Thus started the meteoric career of Frank Sinatra.

* * *

Don't misunderstand me: I do distinguish between Sinatra the idol and Sinatra the philanthropist. He comes to Israel and contributes the entire profits from his seven concerts towards the founding of an ecumenical orphanage in Nazareth. Well and good. But that doesn't exempt him from musical criticism yet, does it? No, because the truth is — we're jealous.

We don't mind his being a millionaire with his own private air force. He gets half a million bucks for a minute on TV? What of it? Frankie gets up at noon, drops in at the studio and sings into the mike: "Hiya, what's doin'?" then goes to the box office, picks up the half-million and can stop working for life. We don't mind any of this. Who said you can only sell dog food or razor blades with publicity, but not a singer?

No, what kills us is the female rapture.

Myself, I'm not all that crazy about movie stars who switch to a new duty-cutie every night. Still, moral reservations aside, I can sympathize with the girls. Six feet tall, three feet wide, millions deep, virile posture and lots of hair, or a sparkling bald pate — where's the woman who can resist that! But Frankie? That underfed chicken? What do all those women see in him? What's so marvellous about him, huh? You tell me, huh?

"Dunno," says the little woman, "He's divine."

So here my wife, my lawfully wedded wife, tells me to my face that this chirping Frankfurter *has* something! I go and fetch the newspaper with his picture:

"What's so divine here?" I yell. "Just show me: what's divine about this guy, huh?"

"His smile."

"All right, so he's got made-in-America teeth, so what?"

My wife looks at the picture and her eyes go glazy: "Nothing," she breathes, "Nothing I wouldn't do for a man who sings like that . . . ."

"He sings?" — I lose my temper — "This picture here sings? All I see is a guy with his mouth open! But singing? You hear singing?"

"Yes," says the woman and rises up in the air and floats around for a while.

* * *

I left the house in a rage and went and bought two tickets to the first concert. *I* want to see that miracle! At home my wife threw her arms about my neck and kissed me for the first time in hours:

"Tickets," she lisped, "For Sinatra. For me."

And right away she got up and hurried to her dressmaker, because after all, she argued, after all she couldn't go to this concert in rags.

"Sure," I hissed, "He'll take one look at your new dress in row 19 and he'll stop in mid-song . . ."

The little one went pink:

"Aw," she breathed, "they don't stop in the middle of a song."

I bought pictures of Marlon Brando, of Michelangelo's 'David', Helmut Schmidt and Ryan O'Neill. Nothing. Frankie and nothing but. "Love looks not with the eyes," as Shakespeare said, and he never was much of a Frankophil either. That night I dreamt that Sinatra was playing the pipe in Tel Aviv, and all the women of the Middle East were flocking to him and leap-frogging gaily over his head (he's only two feet tall).

Next day brought good news:

"Ha-ha," I informed the wife, "your darling Frankenstein is only *half* the bill. He's only on an *hour*. The other half is Yemenite folksongs, and the management offers its apologies to the public."

"Oh" — thus the woman — "a whole hour with Frank Sinatra!"

I took out the magnifying glass I'd bought on the way home and made a close inspection of the picture:

"His wig looks like it's slipped a bit, don't you think?" I said.

"Never mind, he always sings with his hat on anyway."

He does, does he? How sexy! I bet it was designed for him by a special seismograph measuring woman-quakes. He's got a whole pack of court-writers too, has Frankie, who write up his stormy adventures for the daily press. Every word of it true. "You want it frank — take Frankie!" "He Sings Good — Like Sinatra Should!" He's got three professional lady-fainters in his retinue: they go into a trance, and the local ladies follow suit. Also on the plane with him are a couple of scientists, one Rear-Admiral, a portable computer, collapsible bodyguards, body-builders and nobodies. So I wrote on the wall of the house across the street: "FRANK GO HOME!"

The performance was sold out regardless. But time was working in my favour. On Sunday I saw in the paper how Frankie wouldn't sing for even half an hour, just 25 minutes in a low voice, and the rest would be filled by the Ramat Gan Children's Choir, a lecture on biorhythm, and apologies.

"Perhaps it's all for the best," said the smitten woman. "A whole half hour with *him* might be too exciting . . ."

Next day the rumour went round that Sinatra wouldn't sing at all but just come on stage and wave. The rest would be the Heigh-Ho Trio singing hot favourites and cold comfort, apologies.

"In that case," announced the woman, "you'd better turn in the tickets right away . . ."

"At last! Thank God . . ."

". . . and change them for better seats! If he only comes on for a few seconds I want to at least get a good look at him."

The little woman had an appointment with her hairdresser as well. Now I was really getting scared . . . Who knows, maybe Frankie'd appear . . . move to centre stage . . . wave his hand twice . . . 3000 of the town elite get to their feet and applaud like mad . . . Frankie gives a bow and Smile No. 18 . . . The applause swells. Ecstasy. The first ladies swoon. Is there a doctor in the house? . . . Frankie turns – but no! He halts . . . What's up? The celebrated singer steps down into the aisle . . . The lights come on . . . He walks, great heavens, he walks towards me . . . Me? *Me?* Such an honour . . . No, he approaches my *wife* . . . I allow her hairdo is brand new and the dress has a velvet galloon up front, but still . . . "Come," snaps Frankie and his teeth sparkle . . . The wife gets up: "Ephraim, I know you'll understand" . . . and goes . . . a handsome couple, there's no denying it . . . they'd be exactly the same height if my wife took her shoes off . . . and they go to inherit a brighter future . . . I never properly appreciated that woman, and now off she goeth with her lord, she followeth Frankie into the wilderness . . .

Divide and Rule

One morning an old new immigrant like myself may wake up and remember with a glow of satisfaction that he dreamt he was talking fluent Hebrew to his grandma in the town of Hodmezövarsarhely. I'm sure this must be the acme of acclimatization, beating an acquired taste for *falafel* any day. A man does feel the need to do this from time to time – sit back, I mean, and ask himself what's left from his distant Hungarian diaspora days besides the funny accent.

An honest heart-search reveals that yes, one thing has remained: I still *divide* in Hungarian.

Adding and subtracting I can somehow manage in Hebrew, but it's common knowledge that division is only possible in Hungarian. Actually I'm always puzzled how people who don't know Hungarian manage their fractions at all. Amir, for instance, achieves this feat without batting an eyelid, except that now and then he calls on his father to help him with his homework. At such times I must execute a quick double-think for the good name of Hebrew Fatherhood, so I do the sum in my head in a Hungarian whisper, and come out with it aloud in the language of the Bible. No wonder I often get confused in the process, which just goes to show that division is indivisible.

"You're supposed to do your homework on your own!" I tell Amir crossly, "Sit down and concentrate, for heaven's sake!"

After all, it doesn't do to tell my own son that I don't understand a word of what he's saying; that I haven't the remotest idea what vulgar and improper fractions are, not to mention aliquot parts, which somehow sounds like the improperest of the lot.

"Daddy," says Amir, "Is it true that any rational number can be expressed as a decimal fraction?"

"Anything's possible," says Daddy, "It's just a matter of will power. Go back to your room at once!"

These fractions'll drive me nuts. Amir's exercise book is full of the vulgar things. Everything's fractured in there, everything's 1/17th or 38/109th of something else. Once I even spotted 8/6371, a positively morbid phenomenon. No wonder I always feel a wreck after my bouts with sixth-grade arithmetic. A man my age prefers to forget his youth, not keep reviving it all the time.

* * *

And then somebody in America has a brainwave and sets up a Space Research Centre, and the guys there turn out a pocket-computer. Just in the nick of time, too. These midget miracles, the size of a well-developed matchbox, can do sums in their heads easy as pie, and their particular scientific asset is that you can smuggle them through Customs without any difficulty.

So nowadays I keep one of these Japanese know-alls on my desk. It's got a fantastic memory, and whenever I'm stumped by a mathematical problem I play its keys like a well-tempered piano. What's more, I even invent problems just for kicks. It's exhilarating, the things this wonder-box can do. Take a division like this:

378,569.73:63,411.73 =

Just the look of it would have given me the screaming abdabs in pre-computer days. If my future had depended on solving it I'd have said: take my future and leave me in peace. Ever since I got my mini-computer, however, I just feed the whole lot into it, push the buttons and – ping! – it spits out the answer.

There's only one flaw in this arrangement: Amir has got it too.

With his keen animal instinct the child soon sniffed out the immense new possibilities opened up to him by the technological strides I'd taken. A few days after I introduced the Japanese wonder into our household, I caught the brat at my desk with his exercise book open and his hand playing the computer keys like a virtuoso.

"What're you up to?" I hissed at the little button-pusher, "Go do your homework yourself!"

Amir showed me the problem in his book, which went as follows:

"A man bequeathed his property in his will as follows: 2/17 to his wife, 31.88% of the remainder to his eldest son, 49/101 of the remainder of that to his second son, and the rest to his daughter, who received IL71,307¼. How much did each of his other heirs get?"

All I can say is that the late lamented must have been a badly unbalanced character, or maybe he just wanted to take revenge on his family from beyond the grave. My own son and heir has plainly decided to extricate himself from this muddle by way of a simple five-finger exercise.

"My boy," I admonish him gently, "arithmetic is something you do with pencil and paper."

"Why?" asks Amir, "Why work?"

"Because you won't always have a computer by. Like what'll you do if the batteries go dead, huh?"

"Buy new ones."

"And on Shabbat?"

"Borrow Nicky's computer."

"And if he's not home?"

"Then I'll ask you."

He's got red hair as well, my son has. On top of that, each and every one of his friends has at least one computer at home. Their wretched parents sneak them through Customs, taking base advantage of their pocketable smuggability. They're breeding a new generation, a transistor youth who won't be able to divide in *any* language.

As for me, I solved the educational problem with a wave of

the hand. One day, that is, I waved my hand and the computer slipped out of it. Whether it was a Freudian slip or not I couldn't say, but the Japanese divider crashed to bits on the floor anyway. Diveni, dividi, divici.

I knelt and rummaged a little among the dead fractions, and the blood froze in my veins: so help me, dear reader, there isn't a single wheel inside these computers, just a couple of absolutely flat boards with all sorts of lines printed on them. And this, this little wheel-less ninny, can perform complex calculations in a matter of seconds that give me, a writer of standing, grey hairs! How does it do it, the little creep?

They scare me. There's a wee demon inside those computers, no doubt of it.

However, youth is fearless. Amir, at any rate, received the news of the computer's demise with suspicious equanimity. My wife, too, smelled a rat:

"Ephraim," she said to me, "I tell you, Amir's got his own computer!"

So our technological warfare had gone underground, had it? We searched Amir's room from top to bottom drawer. Nothing. The wife claims that Amir's class have a secret hideout at school where they stash the computers. They already make them so small you can stick them in your ear. Anyhow, Amir is suddenly getting top marks in arithmetic, and he walks around smirking like Mona Lisa Jr.

Maybe he's right. The future belongs to computers and midgets. There's nothing left me except swearing softly to myself in Hungarian. Dividing I can't do any more either.

Barely Speaking

The other day I suddenly woke up to the fact that this place is getting full of Swedish nymphs. Up on the cinema posters, I mean. In the movies.

Our cinemas have discovered sex in their old age, and instead of romance and fancy they've started offering us the naked truth. It's got so that you can't cross a street any more without being hit in the eye by little blonde sex maniacs playing footsie with two gorillas or something. We happened to mention as much to Felix Selig from next door and he said yes, wasn't it awful, every morning on his way to work he had to face this enormous . . . you know . . . this *tushy* of a naked wench, splashed all over the front of our neighbourhood cinema, as large as life and twice as natural. I said tsk, tsk, really, and decided to go and see for myself.

I crossed in front of the *tushy* a few times, and even went over to look at the stills: more *tushies* and some breast-work. I thought of the devastating influence all this must have on our youth, and decided to see the movie. Maybe it was the fearful tension of the elections snapping at last, maybe it was all these strikes getting me down. Be that as it may, I felt an irresistible urge to see the Swedish nymphs in the flesh, hip and thigh.

So I decided to go in.

And then a new problem cropped up: how does a respectable *paterfamilias* go in to see a porno movie?

I did once before, but that was in New York, far from the bosom of my family. I had some free time on my hands, and those neon lights were winking hard at me, so I slipped in to see this true-blue movie.

I'll never forget it as long as I live. When I came in, the screen was filled with a close-up of a whatsit, belonging to a faceless floozy who was making her private affairs very public indeed. So there it was, in full colour, six feet in diameter, and with a freelance gynaecologist explaining the works.

My instincts functioned. I shut my eyes tight, rose and fumbled blindly to the exit — too late, though. Under the impact of all that erotica I lost my virility for a week. To this day I mustn't think of New York or tunnels at critical moments.

I decided there and then never to see another pornographic movie.

And now this. The first difficulty was — how do I buy a ticket? The cinema-owner, it's true, was showing some consideration for the Israeli father, and was running his first show in the early morning, when sons are at school. So far so good, but I thought I'd better wait some 20 minutes all the same and sneak in under cover of darkness. Not that I was ashamed, mind you. But still, I preferred not to be caught *in flagrante*. Because I was ashamed, too.

Everything went like clockwork. The first hurdle was the girl at the ticket window. Afraid she'd recognize me from TV, I changed my usual appearance by looking pleasant and cheerful, and dropped my aitches. Then I found myself a good seat in the dark, and began watching with interest as this big black fellow slapped the face of some glamour girl hanging upside down on the wall. Then it suddenly said "Shortly on Our Screen," and the house-lights came on.

The wretched, double-dealing sneaks! Here I had put my trust in this cinema-owner, and he had betrayed me. And for what? To sell a few miserable chocolate bars in the interval? It's lousy management like that that's made our economy what it is.

I hunch my shoulders and squint warily about me. The audience is strictly male, and just about entirely middle-aged and up, though here and there . . .

Omegod, Giora!

The best friend of my own ginger son, Amir. There he sits, right across the aisle from me. Playing hookey to see a porno flick that's For Adults Only. My son's friend, Giora. I'll talk to the principal, that's what I'll do. I mean no, I won't. How do I get out of here?

I take off my specs and cover my face with an abandoned sports-page. How long is this bloody interval going to last? I can just picture Amir greeting me at home with that silly grin on his face:

"Daddy, what's that I heaaar?"

I'll have some explaining to do to the little woman as well. I resolve to get up as soon as it's dark again and clear out of this joint fast.

H'm, easier said than done. I mean, this movie isn't so bad, it's not bad at all. At least the opening scenes are full of promise. There's this average Swedish family, going about its daily affairs: the daughter of the house is in bed with a pimp, while her mother is up to no good with the char on the landing. Next shot: the pimp is making off by way of the drainpipe. On his way down he spots a lonesome lady, bottoms up. He smashes the window and ravishes her in broad daylight and in full detail, but mercifully without any close-ups.

I steal a glance at Giora. He hasn't seen me. I'm almost sure he hasn't. The brat is cracking sunflower seeds with passion, his eyes glued to the screen, no doubt filing data in his mind for future reference. Just now the lesbo ma meets a gay cop in the elevator and rapes him in mid-air, whereas the neighbour, whose tastes run more to necrophilia, gets the hots for the daughter all of a sudden, and I hope Giora's eyes *stay* on the screen.

Is sex necessary?

While I ponder the question, I search around with an eye to eventual escape. The men around me are breathing hard. They all sound as if they have asthma. What's bothering them is: why do we, plain citizens, never slide down any drainpipes and spot any lonesome hotsies?

Me, I did once have a little adventure like that. One evening, many years ago, I was walking down the street when a girl with a cigarette between her lips came over and said:

"Where's you going, Handsome?"

"To Dr. Gruenfeld," I said, and walked on, because that's where I was going, to Dr. Gruenfeld.

Giora! Oh no!

He's seen me. Now he's seen me. Now, just when this hussy, the daughter, has got the char into the bathtub for a bit of slap-and-tickle, this shameless truant turns in his seat and sends me a long look. There's no time to be lost. My domestic happiness lies in the balance. I wait for the next savage rape, then get up and worm my way carefully, seat by seat, to the end of the row. I'm nearly there, only one asthma patient left between me and the aisle, I whisper my last 'scuse-me, and . . . it's Felix!

I scurry back to shelter, and drop into my seat. Felix hasn't noticed me. He's busy. It looks like all the males of our nice residential neighbourhood are in here. Nice residential Sodom and Gomorrah's more like it. I hardly dare lift my head. I also feel my virility going again. This time it'll be a month.

Meanwhile the hussy has gone over to some very sophisticated stuff with *all* the members of her family, plus pimp, plus char. Then up pops Giora, not Giora, this necrophile — and they all tumble into bed and get themselves up into a sort of inverted pyramid, ten bottoms high, and there's no more telling what belongs to whom. It's getting a bit monotonous. I haven't come here to get flesh-poisoning, have I?

I go down on my hands and knees as if I've lost something, crawl past Felix, throw dust in Giora's eyes, and burst out of there with a sob of relief.

Enough. I'll never see another porno flick. Not me. No, and that's final. Maybe I'll just go back to see the end of this movie, and then — never again.

I come home about noon, dead beat. Amir meets me on the doorstep, grinning.

"Daddy," he says, "what's that I heaaar?"

"Well whaaat, stupid?" I yell, "Well what? The editor asked me to do a piece on the spread of pornographic films, so I went and saw a pornographic film. Big deal! You can read all about it in Friday's paper. And meanwhile you can wipe that sneer off your face."

Whippersnapper!

The Joys of Family Transport

Here, at this point, based on long experience, I would like to say that, everything considered, I'm still in favour of marriage. I mean, you work like a slave but you know what *for;* you gradually accumulate a houseful of smart kids, you no longer waste your precious time on every doll, chick, and cutie — in short, you've come a long way from the lone, wretched creature you were in your happy bachelor days. For what does a man crave, after all? He craves for a woman to share life's burden with, someone he can tell his troubles to. So he marries, and from then on he's got something to tell already.

The particular troubles of this writer have to do with travels in the bosom of his family. The way things are I can drive my own car no more than a dozen yards before the little woman gives a loud little shriek, thus:

"Red! *Red!*" Or,

"Watch that bike! *Watch that bike!*"

These sidelong messages invariably come in pairs: the first with a big exclamation mark, the second in italics. Long ago I used to remind my wife sometimes that I hadn't a single traffic offence point against me, that I'd been driving cars practically since childhood, that I had the same number of eyes she had, maybe more, and that I could therefore get along very well without her italics.

About ten years ago, however, I gave it up. I decided it wasn't a question of logic but a purely emotional matter, like the Arabs' hostility towards us. The little woman has four points for traffic offences herself, but with us the Points System does Not Operate.

Sometimes we're driving along a perfectly quiet street and suddenly the little one yells in my ear:

"Ephraim! *Ephraim!*"

In a flash I turn the wheel, mount the sidewalk, hit a couple of dustbins, and crash into the steel shutters of an anonymous laundry. I switch off what's left of the engine and look round me, and there's not a living soul in sight, not one accident-prone vehicle anywhere. This street is as deserted as the Sahara.

"So why did you scream?" I ask my wife curiously. *"Why did you scream?"*

"You weren't concentrating."

And she adds with a groan:

"The way *you* drive! *The way you drive!*" and pointedly fastens her safety belt.

The kids side with Mummy, of course. The first animal my daughter Renana learnt to recognize was a zebra crossing. A *zebra crossing!* Her grandfather, too, likes to point out that I drive like a nut, *a nut*. The other day he took me aside and told me as man to man:

"Look, my boy, you've got your worries and all, why not let my daughter do the driving?"

Even the kids have learnt to declare in chorus from the back seat:

"Daddy, let Mummy . . ."

They keep sending me to all sorts of courses, and shatter my pride in other more subtle ways too. I've noticed that whenever I come home from work Amir calls out:

"It's only Daddy. Nothing's happened."

Why should anything have happened? And why *only* Daddy? Their four-point mother positively eggs them on. On every family drive she hisses: "Oo, will I be happy if a cop catches you now, *Oo, will I be happy!*" Or, "That'll cost you your licence, *that'll cost you your licence!*"

She can only relax, according to her, when she's at the

wheel herself. As often as not she takes it away from me by force with a lot of drama and hysterics and to loud applause from the gallery. To date she's twice smashed into a truck and once into a piano, has felled a parking meter and run over countless cats. Four points.

"That," she explains after every accident, "is because I'm all flustered from your wild driving . . ."

Lately, even Max our dog has joined in the conspiracy like the bitch she is. At every sharp turn she sticks her head through the window and lets out two sharp barks: "Bow! *Wow!*" My wife says she means I should keep *both* hands on the wheel like everybody else.

Sometimes I get my bawling out ex post facto. After I've sailed smoothly and hitchlessly past a couple of peaceful pedestrians, the little woman asks in a voice dripping with irony:

"Did you see them? *Did you even see them?*"

Sure I saw them. *Sure I saw them.* Otherwise I'd have hit them, no?

"What're you doing, for heaven's sake, *what're you doing?*"

"Thirty miles an hour."

"You want to end up in hospital? *In hospital?*"

Her cruising speed is 75 mph., which is just about the rate of her running comment, too. Last month she appropriated the car and whizzed off to the supermarket for some cheese. On the way, a traffic light drove into her head on and turned the car into a recoilless accordion. The little one got out from under, pale but unshaken, though for weeks afterwards her accusing look followed me wherever I went.

"Imagine, you poor thing," the look said, "what would have happened had *you* been at the wheel, God forbid!" She has four points, as mentioned.

After several garage-bound weeks, the car has unfortunately returned to the bosom of our family. My driving has improved a lot, though, ever since I adopted the do-it-yourself method. It's sort of like preventive driving: I myself warn myself at every crossing in order to set the minds of my

250

worried family at rest in advance.

"A stop sign in front of me!" I announce loud and clear while doing 20 mph., *"A stop sign in front of me!"*

Or "Not at amber, Ephraim, *not at amber!"*

And after taking a turn I mumble to myself: "The way I drive! *The way I drive!"*

At least I've got peace in my car now. The wife sits tight-lipped, the kids despise me in silence, the dog barks twice, and I drive me slowly out of my mind.

Barring the Mitzvah

The other day my son Amir turned 13 with surprising ease. He was coached by a qualified rabbi and on the appointed Sabbath was called to the *Torah,* the *Haftarah,* the *Derashah* and other duties, acquitting himself very well under the eye of an unshaven *shamash* — so well, in fact, that when in the end I myself was called upon to bless the Lord for ridding me of him I even felt a moment's doubt. It goes without saying that in the evening we threw a party for good friends, wealthy acquaintances, and dignitaries caught with their excuse down.

Some time before nightfall I approached my son and addressed him solemnly as follows:

"Generations of Jewish ancestors, my boy, look proudly upon you this day, for you have attained the status of mature and responsible citizen of this land, which after 2,000 years of . . ."

"Daddy," the child interrupted me, "You think we'll get to 2,000?"

He's still a redhead, is my *barmitzvah* boy.

"Who's talking of money, cheques, presents?" I scolded him, "What counts is the Event! The *spiritual* experience!"

"I guess I'll open a savings account," mused my son, "In my own name!"

Still, when the first trickle of guests began arriving the mature citizen seemed rather flustered. He didn't know where to stand, he perspired a bit, and he kept asking me what to say. "I'm so glad you could come!" I primed him.

"And when they hand over their present?"

"Thank you, but you really shouldn't have."

The child took up position by the door and set to work. Whenever anyone approached he breathed at them from afar: "Thank you, you shouldn't have," and offered them a rather clammy hand. When he received his first cheque of IL50 I had to grab him or he'd have kissed his benefactor's hand. His pioneer Parker had him in convulsions, and at the sight of a chest-expander he burst into tears of joy.

"Such a sensitive child," said his mother, "His dear little heart just beats like a drum."

The collection-point was set up in my daughter's room, while my eldest son Raphael began sorting the loot. The festive air was spoiled by one stuck-up wholesaler with an exhibitionistic cheque of IL250. Beside this monster-gift all the sets of compasses and encyclopaedias paled into nothingness. Indeed, my blue-eyed boy stopped saying "Thanks-shouldn't," and after a while he even came to me in high dudgeon and complained that two recent arrivals had given him nothing at all, except their hand which they shouldn't have. I got hot under the collar and placed a strict watch on the two worms. It soon turned out that one of them was my son's dentist, the other a worm in a bowtie whom none of us had ever met. They were both stuffing themselves on cake too, the spongers. I sent the kid back to the cheque-post:

"Never mind," I consoled him, "We'll get them yet!"

The pickings were all right on the whole, if somewhat repetitive. Lots of water-bottles, binoculars, and pairs of compasses. Beam-compasses, bow-compasses, compasses. The chest-expanders were spawning like rabbits too. I'd no idea they were so cheap, these spring-things. We positively sighed with relief when the Seligs showed up with a glue-it-yourself plastic boat. "That's better," said Amir.

I myself was kept fairly busy in my function of gracious host, with only brief interruptions for stock-taking. Piles of books were coming in — poems, Picassos, Hadera-Town-of-the-Futures. Also "Behind the Fig Leaf", which is a young

253

person's guide to the hanky-panky. Some idiot had brought a Dictionary of Humour in which I, the child's lawful begetter, wasn't mentioned at all. I gave instructions to withhold drinks from the man.

During a lull in the fighting I experimented a bit with the expanders and found I could stretch two springs without undue strain. I also confiscated a Parker. Take care of the pens and the pounds'll take care of themselves, as my ma always said, and the brat had enough by now anyway. The brat himself stuck to his cheque-post, but his character was changing under my very eyes. He'd given up greeting the crowds, just put out his hand in a mute where's-it gesture. His voice had turned hoarse and quite grown-up. One guest, an architect yet, suddenly contributed IL397.58 and upset our calculations.

On my next visit to the storeroom I spotted two flasks of aftershave. Bah, I say! Also a thick volume entitled "Simultaneous Decay of Free Radicals in Irradiated Proteins", donated by one of my best friends, who told me it was "a fascinating book, science, you know?" "Yeah," I said, "the kid's weak on English though." We were slowly beginning to hate the rabble. To cheer myself I tried stretching three springs and failed. I commandeered another pen, gold-plated, and a mouth-organ.

"For Heaven's sake," the little woman whispered at me, "Do take some notice of your guests too!"

I looked at my sonic barrier at the door. He sized up new-comers with the bloodshot eyes of a Libyan usurer and pronounced with dead certainty:

"Eight at most!"

Or, contemptuously: "Pocket-knife!"

At half past ten he drove us all out of the storeroom and locked the door. "Everybody stay out!" he told us, "It's mine!" The plastic boat proved on inspection to bear a price-tag of IL7.25, whereupon my son searched out Felix Selig in the crush and spat in his eye.

Yet *the* riddle of the day was an anonymous transistor with

254

underwater earplugs which had come with no proof-of-ownership attached. Who the hell had brought it? We checked the list of "Skinflints under IL75" kept up by my daughter, and after a hasty family council decided the submarine marvel must be put down to one of our two unindexed visitors — the dentist or the bowtie. *Which* one of them, though? We were torn by doubt, made unbearable by not knowing which of them to hate and which to shouldn't-have. In the end Amir went on a hunch and kicked the dentist. One up to bowtie.

Finally there was the dubious case of Eldad's pa who'd brought a coloured woodcut of Frankfurt City, with an inscription in ink: "For Eldad, on his *barmitzvah.*" We spilled raspberry juice over the pa. Oops, sorry . . .

"Hey," Amir was greeting the last arrivals, "How much?"

He'd grown into a perfect monster: his glittering eyes were sunk deep into his head, his hands shook with avarice. I broke into the locked storeroom through the window and caught my blushing wife *in flagrante* making off with Golda's Life. I licked my thumb and counted the cheques, and was really shocked by the waste of it. Good Lord, I said to myself, such huge sums of money in a poor country like ours! The mere thought that my son, that whipper-snapper, would now deposit this fortune in the bank gave me a fit. What would it buy him in another 12 years, ha? A fig leaf?

I took most of the cheques and pocketed them. After all, from this day on my son is no longer responsible for his father's sins, right? A man ought to make the most of that. Besides, I had paid for this party with my money. I was the investor, the producer. Let the brat go work.

Feeling quite braced I stretched three springs wall to wall, pinched another five Parkers and an alarm clock, and sneaked back to the mob. The cheque-post was deserted. My son was crouching on the floor and toting up lots of figures with lots of pens. Grown-up, did I say? Grown old, ladies and gentlemen, a stooping old man is this child now, and his hair has gone grey overnight.

Where There's Smoke

Since we became an average suburban two-car family the little woman has a little car. It's a great little car, with just one minor flaw: it won't pull. That's to say — it *will*, but only if you release the hand-brake.

What happens is that the little woman forgets, and that rather interferes with the car's motive power. It sort of twitches, if you know what I mean. Next its tyres begin to smoke too, and then she calls up Micko, our garage hand, from somewhere in town, and tells him:

"Listen, Micko, this morning when . . ."

"Lady," says Micko the Hand, "release the brake!"

My wife's unbrakability does have one advantage: it makes her spottable.

Say I miss her and want to know where she is. What do I do? I go up on the roof, gaze townwards and see a column of smoke — and where there's smoke there's tyres. Very convenient, though not quite original: Red Indians and cardinals use smoke signals too.

* * *

Fortune, however, favours you-know-who, and it accordingly sees to it that the little one's little car won't burn to cinders in the flush of its youth. At the crucial moment, when the car is on the point of cardiac failure — my wife runs out of petrol. She doesn't always run out of petrol, but as near as makes no odds. Then the little car takes a deep breath, coughs once or twice as its lungs fill with air, and stops.

256

Why does the wife of my bosom drive to the last drop, or rather a few yards beyond? Why doesn't she fill the tank up in time? That's a question for future historians to answer. It's a mystery to me.

Perhaps the little one hopes that any minute now they'll find oil in Eilat or somewhere, and the price of fuel will plummet. Or maybe she has faith, maybe she's always secretly expecting a modern Hanukka miracle, when cars will travel for seven days and seven nights on an empty tank.

Meanwhile, though, my wife's car coughs and stops, and as often as not my wife's husband is in the passenger seat, and she tells him:

"Mm, guess I've run out of petrol again. Go get me some, all right?"

This invariably happens right on a busy zebra crossing, and always on Shabbat. What follows is like a classical oil painting: "Man with Jerrican". Its eternal subject is the husband of a woman with a little car. The said jerrican, by the way, is stowed in the boot and is supposed to hold a reserve supply, but my wife forgets to fill it. Or else she forgets to screw the lid back on.

* * *

Sometimes I've fetched her petrol in paper cups, thermos flasks, tennis-ball cans, and once in a cigarette lighter from an emergency pharmacy. Our motto is: Never Give Up. If worst comes to worst, I can always throw myself in the path of an oncoming car and plead with the shocked driver for a few drops of fuel.

This sort of Last-Ditch Fuel is acquired by sucking on a stinking little rubber tube, and it's always the husband who's the sucker. Me, I've sort of developed a taste for the not unpleasant flavour of "Paz Super 94 Octane". Oh well, the petrol shortage is a universal problem, and it won't be influenced either way by an occasional sip on my part.

* * *

Now, don't get me wrong: the hand-brake is something she forgets, but the empty tank is a matter of sober calculation on my wife's part. She's read the manual supplied by the car's manufacturer, and it says there black on white: "When the fuel gauge dial reaches the red line, there will still be enough petrol in your tank for a 6-mile drive."

"Well and good," says the little one to herself, "it's on red, I'm only like six or seven miles from home, so I'll just make it."

Tomorrow morning the engine will swallow air instead of octanes for breakfast and choke to death, but that doesn't bother her. Tomorrow is a long time off, and anyhow – why worry when she's the owner of the original "Man with Jerrican."

Once in a while, say about twice a month, her dial enters the red district, but our house has moved and is now 10 miles away from her. At this point the little woman has two options: she can buy petrol, or she can cut the distance home to six miles and fall nicely within the manual's safety zone.

The first solution is out. The little woman doesn't buy petrol, period. As for the second solution – shortening the way home – the question is: how? Especially as she still hasn't released the hand-brake.

* * *

Don't think the little one's car doesn't have a little red warning light that starts blinking like crazy when the brake is on. It does, but my wife ignores it. Blink-blink – it irritates her, she says. Anyhow, her mind is on the fuel gauge, and she only has one pair of eyes, dammit. She's got to choose her red: gauge or blinker, she can't watch both.

One Sunday, after a particularly long jerrican-trek the day before, I took the little car to Micko the Hand and asked if he couldn't put in some gimmick that would serve as an extra warning, over and beyond the blink. Something that would start ticking loudly when the brake wasn't released, say, or operate a siren, or set off a little explosion. Something.

Micko said he'd been asked to do this before, and it rarely helped. One husband had gone so far as to suggest that he fool around with the wires a bit, so that if his wife forgot the brake she'd be electrocuted.

We thought that was overdoing it, and decided on a musical solution for my wife instead. Micko would connect the brake to a music box, which would start playing the great Toreador March from "Carmen" in case of brake-forgetfulness.

And that's where matters stand for the present.

So if you, dear reader, should one of these days spot a smoking car playing "Carmen" in the middle of Tel Aviv, you'll know that somewhere nearby, facing the music, is the Man with the Jerrican.

Talking Pollytics

In the beginning there was my daughter Renana, thoughtfully pushing chairs under me whenever I came to table. Next my middle son Amir enquired whether I would perhaps like him to wash the car. Then the little woman joined in, volunteering her opinion that I'd been writing some terrific pieces of late.

"Sorry," I told them, "you're not getting a parrot."

The red light had started blinking in my head some time ago — to be precise, on the day the three of them had come raving *en masse* about the parrot my neighbour Selig had bought on the world market. The way they told it, this parrot talked several languages, laughed — a sort of bubbling laugh like Count Dracula, such fun, Daddy — and occasionally went "rrrr" like a real alarm clock.

"It's true," Felix Selig confirmed when I met him, black rings under his eyes from lack of sleep. "You want to buy him?"

I did not. Why should I buy a parrot from Felix when I already have a parrot at home? Yes, because I nearly forgot to mention that one day we suddenly found ourselves *en masse* in old Mr. Zlobnick's petshop, whence we emerged with one promising talent of grey-green plumage.

"Look here," I had warned old Zlobnick, "The beast can talk its head off for all I care, but I want no clocks ringing in my house all night."

Zlobnick gave me his word that our parrot would behave like a human being and only talk.

"Them Grey Africans are the smartest of the lot," he explained. "Listen, this friend of mine, this cop, he told me how one day the phone goes at the station, he picks it up, somebody tells him a large cat has just entered the room, 'So?' says my cop. 'For that you got to call the police?' 'No,' says the voice, 'but this is the parrot speaking'."

Zlobnick roared with laughter, sobered abruptly, and offered me some brief notes on parrot-rearing. A parrot is a grounded bird, he said, fond of company, tickle and tick-prone. You've got to first teach him to perch on your finger, then you can start the talking drill. Every success is to be rewarded with a peanut. And watch out for his bill or he'll nip you, the little devil.

"Devil?" I said. "Maybe it's a she-devil?"

It turned out there's no telling. A parrot has no thingamajig, no nothing, it's a positively Victorian bird. It doesn't breed in captivity, if at all. When you put a mate in its cage it clams up and won't say another word, not even for a banana. Parrots are born bachelors, prim puritans whose sole passion is talk-talk, just like politicians.

"Leave it to me," Amir promised. "In a week he'll greet every visitor to the house with a great *Shalom!*"

At home my son promptly sat down before the cage, put in a finger as instructed, yelled and took it out again, and began the first lesson:

"Say shalom! Say shalom! Say shalom! Say shalom! Say shalom! . . ."

Space doesn't permit reproducing the text in full, but it was Amir who ate the peanuts that night. Throughout the marathon lesson, our parrot kept staring at him with glassy eyes and remained as mute as the goldfish in Zlobnick's shop. Visitors made us feel terrible. "He's a bit out of sorts today," we'd mumble apologetically.

Amir kept it up staunchly for three weeks, at the end of which we decided Zlobnick had sold us a deafmute. We had tried everything. We had pleaded with the animal, scratched, tickled, bribed it with nuts – nothing. Apples – the glass treatment. Our dreams of shalom appeared as unattainable as peace.

* * *

And then, on that unforgettable morning when my important overseas call finally came through and I could hardly catch a word over the buzzing line, I suddenly heard loud and clear behind me:

"Say! Say! Saysaysay!"

So he'd caught on after all, had he, even if he'd rather got hold of the wrong end of the stick. Still, it proved he was teachable, drillable, talk-to-itive. All it wanted to make him speak, apparently, was an overseas phonecall, meaning our bright bird had to feel sure he was being a nuisance.

Amir, at any rate, declared there and then he'd make the obstinate bird say "shalom" or pluck all the feathers from its tail. What's more, my clever boy recorded himself on tape in an endless loop, as follows:

"Shalom! Shalom! Shalom! . . ."

The tape ran beside our parrot's cage till the batteries gave out – nothing. A few days later, on the other hand, right in the middle of the 9 o'clock news, our Polly cocked her head at us and screeched:

"Who! Who-who! Whowhowho!"

What who? Why who? Who who? The beast must be bonkers, said my wife. I myself decided we'd call her Whowho from now on. "We've got to meet the bird halfway," I explained to my family, "shalom or no shalom." No shalom seemed more likely, because on the following weekend Whowho started all of a sudden to bark.

"Bowwow!" she went. "Grrr-wow!"

Our bitch Max must have had a long-distance call. Max herself responded with a fierce back-bark, and since then these two talk to each other all day, except when we have visitors and Whowho clams up.

As against this she's learnt to dance. When you stand before her cage and sing to her about Socra-ha-hates superstar and rock yourself on your feet, then she rocks herself too, though she doesn't sing. She whistles.

She's learnt *that* from the football referees on TV, and practises it between saysays in the middle of the night. Yes, and how many times can a man wake up in the middle of the night from dreaming he's Pele?

So after one particularly berefereed night I dropped in on old Zlobnick.

"Our parrot barks by day and whistles by night," I said accusingly. "You gave me your word!"

"Na," said Zlobnick, "What do you expect? You got to cover its cage at night."

He sold me a thick plastic cover right away, made in Belgium and guaranteed whistleproof. That evening I put the Whowho-hood over the cage, went to bed and slept like a log. Till 3 a.m., when the little woman got up and removed the hood.

"What's this," she said, "a prison?"

She was right, humanely speaking, but I did sometimes feel it was a pity that Whowho couldn't fly. Especially when Renana caught the flu, and our parrot began to cough. She's very attached to Renana altogether, is Whowho, which proved disastrous on one occasion.

Renana is a prudent little girl, and when she's at home alone she never opens the door to strangers without first asking "Whosit? Whosit?" in her childish treble. On that fateful Wednesday it was Whowho who stayed home alone, meaning — without her usual appreciative audience.

At 5 p.m., the laundryman arrived with our washing and rang the doorbell.

"Whosit?" came a childish treble from within.

"The laundry," said our laundryman.

"Whosit?" from within. "Whosit?"

"The laundry!"

"Whosit?"

"The *laundry*!"

"Whosit?"

"LAUNDRY!"

263

This went on for quite a while, the poor man ringing and crying laundry, laundry, and Whowho coming back with this latest variation on her name, "Whosit".

We don't know just how long the drama lasted, but when we came home at 7 we found our garden sprouting underpants, and the rest of our linen on the doorstep, scattered like diaspora Jewry. The laundryman, we heard, had been carried off screaming in an ambulance. We ourselves opened the door carefully, to be greeted by hoarse shouts:

"Laundry! Laundrylaundrylaundry!"

Which, added to the rest, made for quite a vocabulary: "Whowho. Say. Bowwow. Cough. Whosit. Laundry." And one fine day, to come to the point of our tale, history finally did the trick. Along with everyone else, that is, we had been sprawling for hours in front of the television too, watching the long peace-making process from Camp David to Cairo, its endless speeches and ceremonies prominently featuring one single word, peace, you guessed it, shalom.

And that Monday evening, Whowho cracked.

"Shalom!" she screeched. "Shalomshalomshalom!"

Our parrot had become a dove. She's been at it all day since: peace, permanent peace, peace now, shalomshalom. We sent off congratulatory cables to Mr. Begin, President Sadat, Jimmy Carter and old Zlobnick.

Stopping the Gap

Entertainment begins at home. I don't know if this bright slogan has been thought up by any political party yet, but I hereby make them a present of it. As a matter of fact, I'm talking of noise. To be precise, of the fearful din in my own home — the result of having begotten an exaggerated number of children in a careless moment.

Personally I still have a vivid picture of my late father coming home from work every day and switching off the radio first thing. Nowadays it's the other way round: when the head of our household comes home from school, he, my son Amir, casually turns on every switch in the house. Transistor, record player, TV, electric mixer — no matter what, as long as it's got noise-potential.

The new generation likes noise, the louder the better.

I hear that it's a universal phenomenon, that parents all over the world go round with cotton wool in their ears, that it's the young generation's way of getting back at us for the gap in the energy crisis or something.

Be that as it may, when this father comes home and finds that all his pens and pencils have rolled to the floor, he knows Amir has been playing the latest "Rolling Stones" record at the pitch of a Concorde aircraft — which, if you remember, wasn't allowed to touch down in New York at the time.

Every switch in our house is turned up to the bitter end. When Renana, my dainty daughter, is listening to non-stop Boney M., our windows rattle and solid oil paintings drop off the walls. The other day the fridge swung open under the impact of an Elvis revival and, so help me, defrosted.

My neighbour Felix Selig tells me that Travolta has the same effect on their wardrobe. One day, he said, it actually caved in, but his twins didn't blink an eyelid, calmly staying with Travolta in the ruins like so many Hare Krishnas.

"Well," Felix added, "so then I lost my temper and started yelling. 'Dammit!' I yelled. 'Why do you have to have this blasted pop on so loud?' "

"Bravo!" said I, approvingly. "And what did the twins say?"

"Nothing. They couldn't hear me over the music."

* * *

The generation gap at its gappiest. It beats me too. I mean pop, all right. But why at such bedlam pitch. I once revolted against one Fats Domingo or whatever and stalked into the kids' room.

"Enough!" I screamed. "Stop it! Quiet!"

Amir, that redhead, put out a hand and turned the volume up a bit. I grabbed a piece of a paper and wrote with shaking hand: "Cut the racket!" My son took the pencil and wrote back: "What racket?"

Maybe they're just made differently, our kids. Maybe they're born with double-thickness eardrums. Or maybe the evolutionary tide is turning and their auditory organs are slowly growing back into fish gills. Our gilded youth. It's not even music as such. My own three are quite capable of listening for hours to a record whose needle has stuck — Abani-bani-bani . . . Pop, rock, disco — so long as it's loud and continuous. They're good mixers too, my brood: transistor plus TV plus Elvis plus their own fists drumming on the table. The amplifier generation. There are traces of it in the Old Testament already. "Behold," it says in Jeremiah 10, 22, "Behold, the noise of the bruit is come, and a great commotion, to make the cities of Judah desolate, and a den of dragons." Exactly! And that was *before* stereo!

Last week our cat ran away. That was the day Rafi, my eldest, discovered Pink Floyd and his Orchestra. I'm told the town is swarming with deaf cats. When Renana says "Abba", which is Hebrew for Daddy, she's referring to four Swedish singers, not me. Come to think of it, they hardly refer to me at all any more. I'm an old fogey. At best they pity me.

"If I can't have my music on good and proper," Amir explained to me recently, "then I can't study for my exams. I've got to concentrate."

An old fogey, that's what I am. A wet blanket. A square. A fossil. Ah, well, I'm not alone. Every parent I know is going deaf. If this goes on we may well join the dragons in their den.

* * *

Yes, and I see in my paper that the new thing in America is for their youth to go about with a giant box of a transistor playing at the top of its decibels. No doubt they're all studying for their exams.

The Concorde. Don't make me laugh!

My dentist claims they do it on purpose. "They make all that noise," thus he, "because they know we hate it. I always ask my own Danny to turn the volume *up*."

"And what does he do?"

"Turns it up."

When it comes to the crunch, says my dentist, he's got one weapon left. The root treatment, so to say. He's got this faulty lamp at home that produces a short circuit when it's turned on. Satchmo blows his horn – he blows a fuse. It's no good against transistors of course, but even a brief silence in the dark is welcome.

But I'm not beaten yet. I'm a fighter, I am. Like the time Felix's twins did a Saturday Night Fever turn in the garden below. A party they called it. The original madding crowd. By 3 a.m. I'd got to the stage where spies start to sing. I knew there was nothing I could do right away. If I called the police, the only result would be a couple of deaf cops on the force. Next day, however, I went into town and bought myself a big trumpet.

"Please," I told the shopkeeper, "I want the loudest you have. I need it for deterrence."

I took it home and waited with a heart full of spite for the day of my counterblast. Saturday night came, and with it the fever in the garden. I went and stood at my window, filled my lungs with oxygen, and opened my concert with a great fanfare. Me and the big elephants. Between blasts I noted with satisfaction that trumpet blowing wasn't as hard as I'd thought. Any parent can do it, so long as he's angry enough and goes low on the spittle.

"Toot! Too-toot! Whee!"

It went quite nicely with the fever. The crowd in the garden stared up at me in amazement, then sat down on the grass, and burst into loud applause whenever I stopped for breath. I myself improved with practice, and ended with a really magnificent number, and an encore by request. The following morning Amir patted my shoulder for the first time in 15 years.

"The crowd says," he observed, "that my father is okay."

"Ha-ha!" I retorted. "Seems your old man isn't so old after all, what?"

Really, why all this fuss about a little bit of noise?

Claudius and I

I, Tiberius Drusus Nero Germanicus Ephraim, haven't been doing a thing for the past few months except sit in front of the box come Friday and watch this stunning BBC series in instalments.

During the week in between Fridays I'm busy getting up on the who's who of it, by which I mean arguing endlessly with the members of my household about whether Marcellus of the First Part was Octavia's own offspring or that of her husband's first wife, and whether Augustus was Caesar's natural grandchild or his adopted son.

The only thing that's kept this whole weekly bunch together is the strong figure of Augustus' wife, dear old Grandma Livia, who's actually the wife of half the grandpas in the cast, and who in the 186 years of her life managed to poison every Tomis, Dickus and Harrius in the family, except for Claudius who's too dumb to waste good poison on, and who's anyhow rather good-natured in a live and let Livia sort of way.

As for me, I've developed a kind of instinct for guessing who Grandma's next victim is going to be, and spend the empty weeks between Fridays laying bets against the rest of the family. When we got to Part Three, that is, I discovered that it was nearly always the upright republicans who got bumped off. I mean, anyone who looked halfway honest, or who believed in a republican rather than an imperial regime, sooner or later got his deserts at supper.

Our domestic crisis erupted round about Part Four or Five when Drusus kicked the bucket. I don't for the present wish to go into the question of who or what Drusus is or was, suffice it to say that just when Grandma was getting busy in her kitchen, the little woman asked me sort of casually:

"Want some fruit?"

Was it something in her voice, I wonder, or were the gods up there flashing me a little warning signal? Be that as it may, I took my eyes off the poison-screen and stared at the basket of yellowish peaches my wife was holding out to me. Holy Jupiter, I said to myself, why *peaches?* Why the hell peaches which she never buys?

"Go on, have some," the little one urged. "So good for you, darling."

Darling?

I sent her a piercing look and asked:

"How about you?"

"I don't want any. I've a bit of a tummy-ache."

"Me too."

I didn't touch those peaches. Dunno, Livia also seems pleasant enough on the face of it. I'm taking no risks. It's not as if I had proof against the little one or anything. On the contrary, she seems quite all right as wives go, and I'm her lawful husband, after all — but so was Drusus Livia's son-in-law or something and she still poisoned him round about Part Four or Five. I guess it's nothing to do with emotions, it's a question of what the script says. Me, if there's anything I've learned these past weeks it's that a man can't be too careful where his family is concerned. Yes, and Agrippa, R.I.P., ate some fruit as well two or three Fridays back, and look where it got him . . .

* * *

So on that night of Drusus and the peaches, I opened a tin for supper and thought of Friedrich.

Friedrich was our parrot, R.I.P. He was a great talker and we were very fond of him, till the day the poor bird learnt to imitate the sound of our doorbell. How many times can a

270

man get up to open the door and find no one behind it?

"He'll be the death of us," said the wife at last. "We should never have bought him."

One day after that venomous remark, I found Friedrich legs up in his cage. I'll never know what exactly happened, but on the Night of Drusus I recalled the event and, what's more, suddenly began to feel uneasy about a few other strange things that had happened round the house lately.

Like Uncle Egon, whom the wife can't stand because he always forgets to use the ashtray. Sure enough, the other day Uncle Egon pushed back his plate of greenish eggplant salad, gripped his stomach, and stumbled out of the room. We sent for the doctor who could find nothing, but you've only to put ashtray and eggplant together to get the picture. Talking of pictures – they were right then showing the final agony of Gaius and Postumus, who went R.I.P. to clear the way for Tiberius, son of Livia the Ripper.

Good heavens, I thought, can that be what my little one is after – to manage things so that *her* children inherit everything? I didn't sleep a wink that night, and only at dawn remembered that *her* children were *my* children as well, and in that case what were the odds? Just to be on the safe side, I poured my breakfast coffee out into the sink. It did look suspiciously brownish, and it somehow tasted bitterish-sweetish too, and went down the drain with a funny sort of noise, glog-glog-glog.

Next I took the peaches and gave them to the dog. Max refused to touch them! She sniffed, went pale, and slunk off with her tail between her legs.

Aha! I whispered to myself. Aha! From now on I'll only eat what the dog has tasted first. No help for it, I'll have to get used to bones.

All right, but why won't my wife touch the nice reddish cheese I brought her from Holland either?

No-o-oooo . . .

* * *

Augustus died in July of a stomach complaint. Round

271

about the end of Part Six he started to have faint misgivings about my lady his wife, in view of the systematic purge of all his brothers, sons, uncles and nephews, with the sole exception of Livia's pet Tiberius. That night the emperor decided he'd eat nothing but fresh figs straight off the tree, unaware that his little woman had poisoned the tree as well. Me, I announced then and there that from now on we'd only eat in restaurants on Saturday.

"Now? With those price rises?" the little one asked in a funny sort of voice. "Don't be stupid!"

The ghost of my Uncle Sandor of Hódmezovérsérhely appeared before my mind's eye:

"Stay stupid, my boy," Uncle whispered. "Stay stupid and you stay alive . . ."

Meanwhile Grandma Livia herself has finally ripped off too, and the poisoned atmosphere in our house has lifted a bit. Unless Caligula goes and spoils it all again tonight. I hear he never poisons people, he cuts their throats, and that's just what he'll do in the coming weeks to all his relations. Nice prospect for my family, I must say.

Weather Forecast: Scattered Umbrellas

The climate of our country is well ordered; one may even say it is a model of planning. Nine months of total summer, long-play sun without a trace of cloud, two transitional months and only one month of rain, and even that is mostly make-believe. Small wonder, therefore, that the umbrella has not yet penetrated into the consciousness of the population. I personally, former European that I am, sometimes go out with one. But I never come back with it.

Possibly this mixed-up winter is to blame. Because you can't tell whether it's going to start at long last, or whether it's already over. The dark clouds gather and a Siberian wind howls in the streets – and fifteen minutes later the sun shines and the birds are twittering, and after two minutes it's again partly overcast with local showers. During these madcap times it's safer not to budge out of the house without an umbrella. That at least was the view of my little wife as I prepared to go and collect the car from Miko's garage.

"Take my umbrella," the wife said, "and for goodness' sake don't lose it!"

She repeats this warning like a parrot, every time I go out with an umbrella. It's a little ridiculous, really. What does she take me for – a kid?

"Tell me, my dear," I asked her with succinct irony, "when did I ever lose my umbrella?"

"Day before yesterday," thus the wife. "I beg you, don't lose mine as well!"

She gloats over the fact that the day before yesterday I

273

forgot my umbrella somewhere. She is a great one at rubbing things in, the little one is. She exploits the fact that I have to go to Miko's garage with her umbrella. She is insulting me, really, because her umbrella is undeniably of the female gender: lean and blue, and on top, instead of a handle, it has a dog's head made of marble or something. I took hold of the loathsome freak with two fingers and went out into the pouring rain. It goes without saying that when I got off the bus the weather had turned completely summery. The skies were clear, the trees in bloom, nature was awakening, and I was walking on Dizengoff Street with a female umbrella. Naturally the car was not ready yet; Miko said it still had to be tuned up. On my way home I dropped in at the bank and withdrew some cash, then sat for a while at the California and talked with some friends about the crisis of theatre criticism. Then I hurried home because it was nearly 1:45.

The wife stood on the doorstep and asked:

"Where is the umbrella?"

Where was it? I had completely forgotten about it. But where had I forgotten it? Where? Think, man, the main thing was to keep a cool head.

"I left it at the California." It came back in a flash. "Of course, because I clearly remember that I held it between my knees so they wouldn't see it. That's it. I'll bring it, my dear, two minutes . . ."

I dashed straight to the bus stop through the rain which was falling again. Sitting in the bus, I mused on the British, who didn't walk a step without an umbrella and didn't lose it whenever the rain stopped, as a result of which that neat and orderly race had built itself an empire which was falling apart only now. In the grip of such international thoughts I arrived at my destination. I woke up at the very last minute, quickly jumped up, grabbed the umbrella and started pushing toward the exit.

"Hey, that's my umbrella!"

It was a very fat lady who had sat next to me all the time. Absent-mindedly I had taken her umbrella. Things like that happen. It had been lying practically under my hand; so I got a little mixed up, so what? The fat lady kicked up a big roar, called me pickpocket and other pet names. I explained to her that I didn't need her lousy umbrella, that I had several of my own scattered strategically all over town. In any case, I got off quickly and fled for my life. At the California I immediately found the wife's umbrella, or rather its debris. They had tossed it into a corner, trampled it underfoot and dirtied it into an abomination, the barbarians. My heart skipped a beat as I picked up the poor wretch. What would my little wife say? Life had become terribly difficult lately in this country.

"Well, you see," I announced to the little one with forced gaiety as I came into the house, "I found it!"

"What did you find?"

"Your umbrella."

"This is my umbrella?"

It appeared that in the meantime they had sent back my wife's blue umbrella from the bank. Naturally, now I remembered, I had forgotten it at the bank. Of course it was at the bank. Then whose . . . whose . . . this black horror?

The telephone rang.

"This is the waiter from the California," the waiter said, somewhat upset. "They say here that you just walked in and picked up my umbrella. That's not nice. I finish at three and it's raining outside."

"I beg your pardon," I answered, greatly embarrassed, "I'll return it right away!"

The wife was a little nervous.

"Take my umbrella," she said, "but for goodness' sake don't lose it!"

"What do I need your umbrella for? I've got the waiter's."

"And on the way back, stupid?"

Has it ever happened to you, kind reader, that you walked in the street in the hot Mediterranean sunshine with two umbrellas on your arm, one of which was a black parachute and the other ended in a dog's head? It seemed to me that everyone in the bus queue was looking at me pityingly, their eyes saying "Sissy!" I felt relieved when I started sneezing and could disappear into a nearby pharmacy to buy some aspirin. "I won't go back into the street before it starts raining," I vowed, but suddenly my stomach started rumbling, as I had not had my lunch, it will be remembered. I went to the corner buffet, ordered half a portion of falafel and wolfed it down in the bus. The waiter was waiting for me in front of the California. He looked somewhat disappointed.

"Listen," he said, "where is my umbrella?"

That is what he asked me, where was his umbrella. Do I know where your umbrella is, why ask me? And where is my wife's umbrella, you crook? I almost threw myself on him. What's going on here, dammit, all the world's umbrellas get lost in my hands?

"What's the hurry?" I threw at the waiter. "I'm here! You'll have your umbrella in a moment!"

I ran back to the bus in a heavy downpour. It's distressing, really. My wife's umbrella, all right, so I lost it, but the waiter's . . .

I burst breathlessly into the pharmacy.

"Yes," the pharmacist said. "Is this it?"

I grabbed the umbrella and dashed out into the street. To this day I could not swear that it was one of mine. It looked like my wife's, all right, yet I had my doubts. First of all, it was quite green, very short and ended in shiny ebony and a plaque: To *my sister, Dr. Leah Pickler.* I'm afraid it was not my wife's. But I had to return something to the waiter, hadn't I? This is the survival of the fittest, my dear, today me, tomorrow you, it can't be helped. If you don't watch out, you are left sans umbrella before you can say "Low pressure front." It is said that at the Central Bus Station they distribute fresh umbrellas daily. You go and tell them: "I lost my umbrella on Line 94." 94 is a very busy line. "Is this it?" a clerk asks. "This is a rag," you answer him. "Show me something newer."

"Hey, sir!"

The falafel vendor waved me cheerfully to his buffet. And you know what? Resting on his counter, like brother and sister, were the two wayward umbrellas — that of the California crook and that of my widow.

Three. A grand total of three.

Standing in line for the bus, I kept my eyes firmly glued to the ground. Dangling on my strong right arm were three umbrellas, a black one, a blue one and a green one. If at least it would rain! But no, the weather was very fine indeed, a light southwesterly breeze was blowing. I packed the three brollies into a bundle so as to give them a commercial look, as if I were an umbrella salesman or repairman or a collector headed for the Hobby Exhibition, but you cannot fool Jews. Some snotty brats hanging around the bus stop pointed me out and whispered among themselves amid primitive giggling. What sort of youth is this anyway?

In the bus I took a seat way back at the rear, hoping my triplets wouldn't be noticed. Thank goodness there were no comments, people had become used to me. Slowly — slowly I raised my glance and there . . . facing me . . . facing me . . . facing me . . .

Good Lord!

The fat lady. The same fat lady was sitting exactly in front of me. She fixed my umbrellas with a glassy stare and sneered:

"Had a busy day, eh?"

And without further ado she started explaining to her neighbours how she had caught me at noon. "He simply picks up umbrellas and flees. Twenty years ago there were no such types in this country. A healthy young man, well dressed, and steals umbrellas, that's how he makes a living, shame on him." Oblique glances were shot at me. "Cop," someone proposed, "let's call a cop!" The crowd alarmed me, I don't like public appearances. At the next stop I jumped up, elbowed my way to the exit and threw myself into the powerful shower outside. As I picked myself up from the pavement I lifted my two hands beseechingly heavenward.

My two hands?

God . . . on Line 5 . . . three . . . umbrellas . . .

They are on their way to eternity.

I am standing in the downpour with closed eyes, like a present-day King Lear, and don't move. The water pours down my collar right through the soles of my shoes and purifies my sinful soul. Here I stand, from here there is no retreat, let the deluge come, let the whole world perish, I'm not moving from here until springtime.

Hospitality

Some time ago my Aunt Ilka, that excellent old lady, while polishing her floor tiles suddenly hissed with pain and from then on could not stand on her feet. The meniscus or whatever they call it had gone to pieces in her knee, and she had to be taken to the hospital, where she was placed in Ward 14.

The old lady immediately had a nurse phone and order us to her bedside, also impressing upon us her particular craving for cheese sandwiches, which, she said, the hospital gave only to severe heart cases.

The family council decided that I was the right person for the job, and entrusted me with a parcel of cheese sandwiches baked in ashes. I soon found myself in front of the double apron of barbed wire enclosing the hospital grounds. The iron gate was locked, so I politely pounded on it until a burly gatekeeper came out and said:

"Visiting hours only on Mondays and Thursdays from two-forty-five to three-thirty."

"I see," I replied, "but now that I am here . . . "

"My dear sir," thus the gatekeeper, "believe me: this is in the patients' interest. Visits excite them and delay their recovery. Just imagine what would happen if we let in anybody any time!"

"How right you are," I heartily agreed. "That would really be terrible. Now let me in, please."

"No," he said. "I was told not to let anybody in or out, so you'll pass only over my dead body."

"Heaven forbid! And now please let me in to see my

Aunt Ilka."

"Nothing doing, sir. I'll be relieved at two. Perhaps the other chap will let you in."

Realizing that the man was a callous fanatic, I turned on my heel and hated him as I had not hated anybody before.

"Drop dead, you maniac," I cursed. "I'll get in to see Ilka if it's the last thing I do on this earth."

Two hours later I came back to the gate, but did not repeat my former mistake.

"I'm from the *Jerusalem Post*," I said to the new gatekeeper. "I'd like to write a feature on the hospital."

"Just a moment," thus Gatekeeper Number Two. "I'll call Dr. Giventake."

The doctor, a very pleasant man, received me most cordially and volunteered to show me around. I said to him, "Don't trouble yourself, dear Dr. Giventake, I'll walk around by myself. That's the new reporting system, you know: spontaneous impressions."

"No, no, it's really a pleasure," Dr. Giventake insisted, and took my arm. "Only I can give you all the information you need."

He then dragged me through Wards 11, 12, and 13, all the while stressing the great role the press could play in educating the public to a better understanding of the medical profession. I hummed my assent and from time to time jotted into my notebook: "Twinkum, twankum, twirlum, twitch. My great-grandam, she was a witch" or words to that effect. The exemplary order that reigned in the wards was marred only by the crowd of visitors: a family or two were sitting on every bed.

"As a matter of fact, visiting is forbidden just now," Dr. Giventake explained. "I don't know how all these people managed to infiltrate."

"It really doesn't matter," I assured him as we walked on, but then an elderly lady hailed me from one of the beds.

"Hello, Feri. Did you bring the cheese?"

It was a most awkward situation. Dr. Giventake looked at

280

me askance.

"*Shalom,* Aunt Ilka!" I exclaimed. "What a fantastic coincidence!"

"Coincidence? Didn't the nurse phone you? Where is that cheese?"

I gave it to her and tried to convince Dr. Giventake that I always had some cheese on me, but he only shrugged a resigned shoulder and left us.

Aunt Ilka gobbled up the cheese sandwiches and ordered peppermint candies for the next day. She also insisted that I bring Bernhard and Mitzi along, to say nothing of my wife. I told her no visitors were allowed, but Ilka shrugged this off with "Everybody's coming."

At home we got busy. Mitzi sewed small white caps, on which she embroidered red shields. The hairdresser lent us three white gowns, and with the aid of two broomsticks we improvised a stretcher. A taxi took us to the vicinity of the hospital, where we slipped into our disguises. Sent out on patrol, my wife reported that the burly maniac was again on duty. I lay down on the stretcher and was covered with a sheet, after which Bernhard and Mitzi began lugging me toward the gate, while my wife held my hand and from time to time moistened my parched lips. The invasion came off without a hitch. The maniac was taken in by this simple trick and opened the gates. We staggered across the grounds, for safety's sake passing through various wards, and had just come in sight of Ward 14, when suddenly the sheet was pulled off.

"You again?" Dr. Giventake bellowed. "Are you crazy?"

"This is no time for joking," I moaned. "I'm dying."

"What happened?"

"Snake bit me . . ."

Dr. Giventake blanched and dragged me into his office. Quickly I gave the peppermint candies to Bernhard and whispered:

"Best regards to Ilka."

My wife and her parents took French leave and left me in

Giventake's clutches. The good doctor opened a number of phials and informed me that he was going to pump me full of curare, the only sure-fire antitoxin for snake poison. By then all my interest in Ilka had vanished. Did I really have to let them poison me just because my aunt wanted peppermint candies before her operation? I hopped off the stretcher, ran out, and clambered aboard one of the small trolleys circulating between the wards.

"Let's go!" I threw at the driver. "Never mind where, just get moving!"

Later I mingled with the host of visitors and escaped, rejoining my family in the evening. Ilka was feeling fairly well, but had somewhat resented my absence and insisted that I bring her some Swiss magazines. Mitzi proposed that we dig a tunnel under the barbed wire, but that would take at least three days, and we could not possibly leave Ilka for so long without visitors. In any case it was clear that mass visits were now out of the question: only one-man commando actions were still feasible. I therefore got into my hairdresser's gown with the buttons at the back, put on thick glasses and a pastry cook's cap. When I got out of the taxi and saw that the gate was again held by the maniac, I tied a handkerchief round my face, and with ringing Teutonic steps approached from the north. The maniac stood rigidly at attention, so I threw a *"Jawohl!"* at him and rushed through Wards 11 and 12 as if I were inspecting them. And then, just as I was about to enter Ward 13, a strong hand grabbed me.

"Thank God, you are here, professor. Please come at once, an urgent operation . . ."

"Sorry, Dr. Giventake," I mumbled behind my mask. "I'm off duty."

"This is an emergency, professor," Dr. Giventake said as he dragged me into the operating theatre, where I quickly washed up and was pushed under the klieg lights. The patient was wheeled in, I lifted the sheet, and Aunt Ilka said:

"Did you bring the Swiss magazines?"

"She's hallucinating," Dr. Giventake remarked, and quickly

had Ilka put to sleep. To be quite sincere, I did not feel too well, because I had never before operated on my aunt's meniscus. The nurse asked me whether I wanted a small or a big scalpel, so I said to Dr. Giventake:

"Take over, please."

Dr. Giventake blushed with pleasure, because never before had a professor given him free rein with a patient. He began cutting up Ilka's knee, and I immediately felt sick as I do even when my wife cuts up chickens' legs in the kitchen, though I eat them, especially if served with cucumber salad.

"Excuse me," I said, and went out. Feeling rather dizzy, I lowered my mask and took a deep breath of fresh air. Just then the maniac passed and patted me on the back.

"You see," he said. "Now you can visit your sick aunt."

I had completely forgotten that it was Monday and between 2:45 and 3:30, though I should have noticed that there was not a single visitor in the hospital grounds.

Relatively Speaking

When all is said and done, nothing cheers a man up as much as discovering distant Jewish relatives he never knew he had, uncles and cousins popping up suddenly on the edge of the vast family map. Near relatives, one's grey everyday kith and kin, are dull by comparison. They're the establishment, so to say, known, confirmed, irrevocable. Not so the others, the unsuspected sister-in-law of your paternal aunt, the anonymous niece on the distaff side — those wondrous border cases whose best part is their out-of-the-blue appearance.

Take the case of my neighbour Felix Selig's father, old Grandpa Selig of Riga, who one day on a bench at B.G. Airport met the brother he hadn't seen in 53 years. Think of it: 53 years. Grandpa Selig cried "Grisha!" and the two brothers fell on each other's neck sobbing. Next they fell to raking up old memories, till Grandpa Selig remembered suddenly that he'd been an only son, whereupon his brother remarked tearfully that he had been born in Australia himself and was called Harry Zonshein. A moving scene ensued, for who'd ever imagine that two perfect strangers who hadn't seen each other in 53 years would suddenly meet like that!

The two stayed talking on that bench all night on account of a ground crew's strike, discussing their uncommon past and the strange twists of fate, and they correspond to this day and call each other by their first names.

* * *

Now, a thing like that only happens due to this irresistible urge people have for discovering long-lost relatives. It's a search for roots, essentially, if possible wealthy roots. The long-lost-relative syndrome is always more prominent in the wake of wars and when the bank demands guarantees.

We still remember the touching story of a certain new immigrant, N.I., who'd been an expert ice-hockeystick mender in the Diaspora. It follows that when he came here, he felt an urgent need to find a certain cousin twice removed. Well, Mr. N.I. went around asking and probing and digging for roots, till he finally discovered his beloved relative, whereupon he flew over to Paris to see him and fell sobbing on the neck of the Baron Rothschild, who kicked him downstairs.

The moral of the story is: Poor relatives have a better memory. But personally, as I said, I'm very fond of distant relatives. You'll admit it's thrilling when someone turns up suddenly on your doorstep and announces: "I'm Sandor, the youngest son of Helga who married the late Immanuel Shmulewitz's nephew." It's positively intriguing, a thing like that. Your heart starts beating, your mind races: Who sent him, this Sandor? Where's he been all this time? Who is Immanuel Shmulewitz?

* * *

The other kind of relative is represented by my Aunt Ilka, once removed but I don't know on which side. Twice a year my mother asks me: "Have you been to see Ilka?" and twice a year I tell her that I haven't but I will. It's not that I've anything against Aunt Ilka as such, except that she lives way out in Jaffa and that she's 89 and a cross old nag. Like when I do show up, the first thing she says is: "So you finally remembered your old aunt, huh?"

"I've been terribly busy," I apologize in my remotest relative voice, "but I'm here now, Aunt Ilka."

So then she tells me to wipe my feet. That's on account of her tilomania. She's mad about her spotless floortiles, is Aunt Ilka, and they look as if she cleaned them with a toothbrush. You cross her doorstep, you're afraid to move on. You wish you could float or something. I've heard it said that Aunt Ilka knows each of her floortiles personally and refers to them by the chessboard system: "G18 is still wet."

After a while we get off the tiles and onto cats. Auntie's eyes glaze over and she whispers: "Ach, Bianca!"

Bianca is her unforgettable tabby that died of old age in the late 'forties. I never met the immortal Bianca myself, because I still lived abroad then and didn't keep track of the fate of Jewish cats. Aunt Ilka fetches an old photo from her antique chest between D21 and F24, and informs me wheezily that "she always used to sit on this very chair you're sitting on now." She says that even when I'm standing on my feet.

I come over respectfully to look at Bianca's photo, and I see a cat. Tail. Whiskers. A cat. I'm a dog man myself.

"She loved you, Robert," says Aunt Ilka, "more than anyone else in the world."

She's 89, is Aunt Ilka. Maybe even 90 already by press-time. I tsk-tsk sympathetically. It's a shame I never knew Bianca, a shame I'm not Robert, a blooming shame.

* * *

Whereas Ilka is an aunt to be visited, Kalman is an uncle to be rung. Rather, he rings me up every so often and asks: "Why don't you ever ring me up?" Uncle Kalman has lumbago too, a disease that lends itself to long and detailed description. It's owing to my Uncle Kalman's lumbago that I ordered this special telephone with a magnifier attached, which does away with the need to hold the receiver to your ear, thus leaving your hands free.

The way it works is this: Uncle Kalman offers me a complete bulletin on his back, and meanwhile I sit and write a play or two, take a nap, trim my nails, do a few push-ups, and everything's fine as long as just every 15 minutes I say "You don't say, Uncle Kalman!" into the receiver. In short, I manage, but it's a bother.

Relief came one day after a particularly drawn-out session with my LP uncle on the phone, when I went out for a breath of air and saw my neighbour Felix taking leave of a sombre old fellow. I watched them embrace silently but with warmth, and then the old fellow walked off without a word.

"That's old Wertheimer," Felix explained to me, "An uncle of mine, I think."

I asked was he deaf or something.

"No," said Felix, "just taciturn. Can't get a word out of him. He bores me to death, does my uncle."

I licked my lips. "Look here," I told Felix, "I have an uncle of about the same age, in good condition, who talks a mile a minute. What say?"

We swapped uncles then and there, and now Uncle Wertheimer drops in on me occasionally to sit in a corner of my study and stare mutely at the ceiling, whereas Uncle Kalman rings up Felix every Monday.

A happy arrangement all round, give or take an uncle. Even my mother approves: "So long as Kalman's got someone to talk to," she says. No doubt of it, the future belongs to the relative swap. Next Friday I think I'll put an ad in the paper:

"Trade-in: My spotless old aunt with dead cat, for an untidy cousin under 50."